ELECTRO GIRL

Lainie Chait

LIVING A SYMBIOTIC EXISTENCE WITH EPILEPSY

This book is dedicated to the most devoted angel in my life, my mum, Helen Chait, for always providing me with a room in her house, love, nourishment, generosity, uncompromised support on every level and the special Jewish pickles she supplied me on tap which helped make this book even more awesome.

Published in Australia
by Raw Encounters Media
electrogirl55@gmail.com | www.electrogirl.com.au

First published in Australia 2017

National Library of Australia Cataloguing-in-Publication entry

Creator: Chait, Lainie, author.

Title: Electro Girl : Living a Symbiotic Existence with Epilepsy/Lainie Chait; edited by Stephanie O'Connell.

ISBN: 9780646947747 (paperback)
ISBN: 9780648043102 (ebook)

Subjects: Chait, Lainie.
Epileptics - Australia - Biography. Epilepsy in youth - Australia.

Other Creators/Contributors: O'Connell, Stephanie, editor.
www.facebook.com/FigmentFriendlyEditing | figment.editing@gmail.com

Cover Photography
Portrait Store/Jason Malouin

Cover Design
The Love Press | www.thelovepress.com

Disclaimer

All care has been taken in the preparation of the information herein, but no responsibility can be accepted by the publisher or author for any damages resulting from the misinterpretation of this work. All contact details given in this book were current at the time of publication, but are subject to change.

The advice given in this book is based on the experience of the individuals. Professionals should be consulted for individual problems. The author and publisher shall not be responsible for any person with regard to any loss or damage caused directly or indirectly by the information in this book.

CONTENTS

Life should not be a journey to the grave with the intention of arriving safely in an attractive and well preserved body, but rather to skid in sideways, body thoroughly used up, totally worn out screaming "Woo Hoo, what a ride!"

Anonymous

Introduction

Happy Birthday to you, Happy Birthday to you, Happy Birthday dear Lainie, Happy Birthday to you. It was my 19th year of existence on the planet and I was about to receive a very special present, one that I would remember for the rest of my life. On this 19th year of existence,... I was gifted a diagnosis of epilepsy! I unwrapped the diagnosis, tried it on for size, worked out that it didn't really fit me that well and that I wanted to return it. "Thanks but it's not really my colour". My personal translation of what the doctors told me was, "Oh, you know the fun, carefree, childlike life you have known up to now? Well, it's going to be all about doctors' appointments, countless tests and medications from now on. No more unaccounted for fun because you need sleep and the meds may cause side effects, so you might be drowsy, feel suicidal at times, break out in unsightly rashes and put on weight but hey... you won't have seizures! Great then, see you in three months for a check-up." WTF?

The seizures I experience are a random expression of my brain that can turn me from conscious to unconscious in a matter of milli-seconds due to the electrical storm flowing through my brainwaves at that moment. Turn me from a totally strong warrioress with bulging biceps, into a play-doh princess needing assistance to wipe the drool and maybe the gravel or grass off my face.

At different stages of my life I rebelled in different ways against this diagnosis, (as you'll find out as you read on), but the most common form of rebelling, which I have finally addressed now, was the non-acceptance of self and the embarrassment, shame and isolation that went along with it. The irony is that as a general rule of thumb, people usually rebel to be different from everyone else, to make a statement of their individuality, to stand up and say, "I will not be boxed in." For me, however, the rebellion was in an effort to be the same as everyone else! "I am not an epileptic, I'm not sick, I'm just like you but I have occasional seizures," I would repeat this over and over in my head in a desperate attempt to try and make this my reality.

I conjured up the idea of writing a book 16 years ago about my journey, not just with epilepsy but the whole journey of life after diagnosis of a condition. So for years, without much thought or passion as to where it would lead, I just kept journaling my life exper-iences and documenting occurrences of seizures, and what was going on at those times. Was I menstruating? Was I emotional, tired or stressed? Had I been partying? Had I slept properly the night before? What had I eaten?

It's been a long and emotional rollercoaster my family and friends have been on with me. Naturally, I could only see what was going on from my eyes, and it's been really interesting to ask some of my close network to write a few testimonials for my website from their perspective as *they* experienced my journey. I have actually encouraged them to say it how it was and not sugar coat the stories with frilly paper, unicorns, and mung beans, even if it makes me seem like a completely stubborn mother fucker. The fact is, I was at times! A very electric one at that! I didn't have the maturity or understanding to look at my story from another's perspective. It was me who was suffering with this, me who was struggling, me who was manipulating people and my surroundings so that I could still hide my "secret" from the world. I thought, by extracting myself from people every now and then and moving from place to place, that I would be taking the burden off any one person to look out for me and it wouldn't be so confronting for all concerned.

I can now see that it was a burden regardless of whether I was there or not, as people who love you worry about you all the time whether you are with them physically. All of us know someone with an illness or a condition and we watch their struggles and wins from the sidelines, just doing the best we can to support them. When you're the one who is being watched, you generally don't think about how it affects the people who are watching you.

My intuition in this whole journey has been to fight for my freedom. Freedom from my own mental incarceration, freedom from what others thought might be the best for me and freedom from the shackles of a one treatment only, medical management system that doesn't encourage an individual to venture outside the pharmaceutical "square" of treatment.

My heart goes out to all who are afflicted with seizures, in particular as this was my journey. I know what it feels like to have the wind knocked out of you by being diagnosed with epilepsy at a young age, but this book was really written to share with everyone who has ever been diagnosed with any condition. If you are a parent of a teenager who is struggling with finding themselves after diagnosis please encourage them to read this book so they can refer to this as an empowerment tool.

This book was written with YOU in mind, so YOU can feel connected to hope and encouraged to believe in yourself, be proud of who YOU are and empower yourself to make paths to have a say in what treatment feels right to YOU.

Thanks to all my patient watchers and angels for making me feel loved and not like a freak - I love you all! Thanks to you the reader for making time to read this and I hope that on some level it can be an inspiration for you to rise up and be a part of your own health solution. It's now time to take you on a journey of my life. All aboard!

I want people with epilepsy to know that there are ways in which they can play a role in their own recovery. It's all in how they approach what is happening and how they can use that as a catalyst for their own growth. If there's one thing that I've learned, it's that people are willing to embrace you if you share your story.

Danny Glover

CHAPTER 1

Electro Girl

I created "Electro Girl" as a fantasy, super hero persona for myself at the age of 16, to help me accept my neurologically electrical flaws, and try to make as much light as possible out of a situation that I was trying my hardest to avoid dealing with. She was never introduced to anyone in my teens as there was no impending danger or harm to myself in those years with the symptoms I was experiencing, so there was no real need for her to cruise down on her lightning bolt hovercraft and save me from anything. She was extremely good looking, had a great butt, and came complete with a cape and a big lightning bolt on her chest, sparkly silver antennas, and a resilient personality that took no shit. As we grew older and faced more challenging circumstances together which were peppered with danger, she became my strength through the hard times and always managed to swoop in and carry me off to safety, eventually. It was therefore a no-brainer that this book should be named in her honour.

I was born in June 1972. For those of you who like Astrology and are interested in the Chinese Zodiac, I am a Gemini Rat. The Gemini part is my Western horoscope and the Rat is taken from Eastern Chinese Astrology. The personality traits that specifically relate to this combination include being an inquisitive knowledge seeker who bores easily and is always overflowing with curiosity. It would stand to reason then, why I have spent the last 20 years and endured over 250 Grand Mal seizures in my efforts to try and understand the scientific, chemical and emotional reasons behind why I have epilepsy, rather than just accepting it as a diagnosis when I was 19. It was evidently written in my terms and conditions when I signed up for this life that I would take the long road to understanding, surrendering, and accepting myself as I am (medical condition and all), so I could finally be at peace at the end of my journey on earth.

Mum claims that she was in labour with me for about 10 minutes. Apparently, I could not get out of her vagina quickly enough. Nine months of being in the same place was starting to bore me, so out I came, eager to see what the world had to offer. From a very young age I was always on the lookout for things to do that were exciting and didn't stem from the average. I was a bit of a tomboy, so if there was an opportunity to climb a tree, jump in puddles or horse poo, play in the mud, or compete in games or sports, I would be right up there trying to prove myself, not because I had to, but because I loved it. I'm not sure if it was the competitive streak in me or my passion for winning that drove me, but whatever it was, I had lots of blue ribbons in my cupboard for coming first in swimming, javelin and shotput amongst other things but my personal favourite was how close I came to blitzing the grade six spelling bee competition. Nothing wrong with second place – apparently!

I didn't stop at sports either, I was in school plays, the school choir, had a crack every now and then at the debating team, tried ballet, attempted piano, but was always looking for something else exciting to sink my teeth into. It was my love of variety that fuelled me to do all these things. I was curious and I wanted a bite out of everything. I had the good fortune of being able to get along with all sorts of people as well, and so socially I didn't have to deal with being an awkward kid that no one wanted to hang out with. My haircuts were awkward, particularly the mullet look I created at age 12, but I was not!

I grew up in a Jewish middle class family in Melbourne, Australia. My parents were fabulous providers and socialites and had quite a good eye for fashion and décor. One of my favourite things to do was go exploring in my mum's wardrobe and troll through all her amazing outfits knowing that someday, I'll be stealing all of them for myself. I have two sisters, Nicki my older sister by 22 months and Chandra my younger sister by three years, and like any siblings, we laughed, cried, fought, scratched, bit and swore at each other for most of our young lives, but we were also very protective over each other. We lived in this really great house, with a pool, sauna, a lemon tree, and a fake patch of grass out the back where we lathered oil on our skin and lay in the sun until we burnt, which was of course acceptable back then as no one even knew how to spell "Ozone layer", let alone worry about what it meant. Inside was decorated with the funkiest furniture from the 70's and 80's. One particular couch set that holds great memories was covered in leopard print and came with a matching life size poof, that if jumped on, you would melt into and could disappear into another time zone.

We were sent to a private school, learned about our Jewish traditions both in and outside of school, and didn't miss out on much, materialistically. We embarked on wonderful family holidays both in Australia and overseas, had family weekends away with other families and their kids, and had the whole middle class routine pretty much down pat.

My grandparents owned a farmhouse in the country which nobody lived in but which was open to anyone in the family at any time. My Zaida, (an informal Yiddish word for grandfather), was quite partial to a bit of horse-racing and having a bet so he bought this hobby farm, I guess you could call it, and kept racehorses that he would race at the local track every now and then.

We used to go there a lot as kids with my aunties, uncles, cousins and grandparents. I have very fond memories of this farmhouse and what it represented for the family unit at the time. On weekends, basically as soon as the car pulled in to the farm, I'd be out the door and off to see the horses, play in the haystacks or go riding on the back of the tractor with Trevor, the farm hand. I'm glad that I had the opportunity to get up close and personal with animals at such a young age, as this was another great love of mine which ended up becoming a career in later years when I became a Certified Veterinary Nurse for a stint in the 90's.

When I was nine, things slowly started to change because mum and dad decided to get out of the shmatta business (another Yiddish word meaning clothes/rags) and bought an inner city restaurant/fast food diner. They both worked long hard hours in the hospitality industry and never really saw much of each other outside of work. We saw mum more as she generally did the day shifts at the diner and then took care of us at home at night. We didn't see dad as much as he worked the night shifts and was usually gone when we got home from school and asleep when we got up the next day. When he wasn't working, he'd be shitty, tired and angry and he was slowly changing into a very different man than the one that he was before the business started. Opening the restaurant was a business decision designed to make enough money so they could afford to give us a comfortable life. I'm not sure either one of them banked on losing so much in the process.

Slowly, the family unit that had seemed so solid, began to show its cracks to the outer world, and none of us dealt with it well. Our disintegrating family unit was a hard thing to deal with for me personally as I had such an emotional gaping hole where my parents used to be; Nicki and Chandra had different relationships with dad so their reaction to him leaving was different to mine. Nicki basically hadn't spoken to dad for two years before he left due to let's say, "personality differences", so to her it was simply a relief when he decided to go. Chandra was feeling turmoil like I was but more because she felt it was her fault he was leaving more than sad that he was going. It was around this time that I turned to the elephant as my protector animal. The symbol of the elephant represented to me this feeling of loyalty to family, which is a trait that elephants display strongly in their herds. My herd was changing around me, but connecting to this elephant energy allowed me to never forget the feeling of the herd strong in my heart, and when I was 20, an elephant took up residence on my perky left breast as a tattoo. Nowadays it still sits on my breast but it is sort of down near my belly button. The important thing is that the symbolism is still strong to me no matter where my breasts end up as I age.

My behaviour started to change and I began to rebel and lie, but I'd always get caught out and the only way that my parents could maintain control over my growing rebellion was to ground me. Indeed, I was grounded a lot between the ages of 11 and 14, and in hindsight I can see that my actions were not only a part of my rebellious and fun nature, but were also an attempt to get their attention and shake some shit up, maybe punish my parents for working so hard and not being around enough.

I remember ringing them from a Jewish youth movement camp asking if I could have a few friends over for an after camp party at our house. They were entertainers so I thought they would surely nurture this side of me. We had the pool and the spa, so my mind was filled with images of a fabulous party. I told them that there would only be maybe 20 people and they agreed. I knew there was going to be more but if I told them there were 80 people coming, it would never have happened. The strict instructions were, "absolutely no alcohol in the house." A sign was even posted on the door to ensure everyone understood these so-important rules. As teenagers though, "no alcohol in the house," meant everyone got blind drunk in the street and *then* came into the house with no alcohol. I think about 100 people turned up and of course it got out of control.

Dad was at work for most of it, but when he got home the shit hit the fan, large. I was so drunk by that stage that when he brought me into the house to lay down the law, all I could hear was a mumbled cacophony of words that were fused together. I couldn't comprehend a thing. Pretty much the only thing that I heard was that I was grounded for the rest of my life. At the time, I was completely high-fiving myself on the inside, and all I could think was, "That was so worth it, everyone had such a good time!", even though I felt a little bad about putting my parents through the turmoil. When it came to socialising and wanting people to have a great time, putting on a great party was what became important and to this day I am still exactly the same. Of course the house looked like road kill the next day but, as I was grounded for the rest of my life, I had a lot of time to clean it up.

By the time I was 14, the very successful business my parents had created was sold and the marriage was over. Mum and us three girls stayed in the family home and dad packed his stuff and moved out. As if these events weren't enough, another very significant shift happened within me that year that turned my world even more sideways and changed the course of my life forever. The beginning of the "head hiccups". I will refer to "head hiccups" a lot throughout the story as the electrical misfires that occurred in my brain which caused a type of short circuitry or momentary electrical imbalance within. They would often happen in the shower when I was getting ready for school. Some days, as I put my head underneath the hot water to wash my hair, I would experience these weird head hiccups (electrical misfiring in my brain). Before I knew what was happening I would be picking myself up from the shower floor, completely at a loss as to what had just happened. The reason for hitting the floor, which I didn't know at the time, was that my legs involuntarily buckled due to the misfiring in my brain at that split second, and if I was holding anything in my hands, that would drop to the floor as well. In the medical world, these are known as tonic clonic jerks. I did a very good job of hiding the falls in the shower from the family, even when the crashing sounds from the falls were so loud that someone would knock on the door and say, "Are you ok? What's going on?" I would respond that I had dropped the shampoo bottle or soap, everything's fine, and no one questioned it. Sometimes those responses were from the floor of the shower, having just had my legs drop from under me, where I was clearly not OK and definitely should have alerted someone to this, but I didn't want to send out panic buttons so I chose to keep it a secret.

Over the three years that these symptoms continued, they never really morphed into anything more than the head hiccups in the shower and the "drops" at times. It was rare for me to experience these in public, but they did occur from time to time. As such, I became a master of hiding the truth. If they happened in public, I would treat it like it was a normal diaphragmatic hiccup and to the outer audience, they would think nothing of it. What they would witness was a body jolt and a noise, which looked and sounded exactly like a hiccup. Little did they know that the hiccups they were seeing were stemming from my head not my diaphragm, and that's exactly how I wanted it. If someone did question it and look confused, I'd say "Wow that was a big one!" or "How weird was that?!" We'd laugh and continue on.

My reasoning for not telling anyone was simple. Due to the meltdown of the family unit, I was going through a lot of inner turmoil - I didn't want to add to that turmoil by publicly outing my symptoms. If people knew what was going on, they would want me to do something about it, like talk about my feelings or see a doctor and I was opposed to either of those things, plus I convinced myself that I was handling it just fine. I didn't want to be singled out, I just wanted to blend in with the crowd, which is ironic because my larger than life personality never really blended in, it always stood out.

The singling out eventuated in the end as my school work started to suffer and I was becoming a disruption in class. Both my parents and the school convenor decided that I should change from the school I'd been at my entire life to a new school, in the hope I'd at least pass Year 12. I did my final two years at an all girls college and my only real memories of that school were making a very dear friend Rachael and being privy to seeing my first violent bitch fight between two girls in the common room. After witnessing this fight I decided to stay out of the way of the "bitches" and get out of that school with my VCE, and my teeth still in my mouth.

People will do anything no matter how absurd,
to avoid facing their own souls.

Carl Jung

CHAPTER 2

Shhh, it's a Secret

As previously mentioned, I'm Jewish. Ours wasn't a religious home, but my parents and grandparents wanted us to learn, understand, and embrace the history of Jewish people and the trials and tribulations they'd overcome throughout history. This was particularly important to my Grandfather as he was a survivor of the Holocaust. As people fought to save young adolescents and children from the demise of the Jewish people, his Father became aware of a lottery choosing 20 boys to be transported to Australia in 1936, out of hundreds of boys he was selected to be one of the 20. He was 14 at the time and boarding that boat for Australia meant his freedom, but it also meant he would never see his family again. I feel very privileged to be born into this story as he and my grandmother forged a new bloodline from scratch, of which I am one of 42 members. The other side to this coin, though, is that there is really no medical history documented on either side of my family for reference to any genetic links to epilepsy.

I went to a Jewish school for 12 years, where I was taught about the culture, the Bible, and also how to speak Hebrew, which I'll always be thankful for. Learning a second language was a pain in the ass at the time, but it turned out to be a blessing in disguise later in life when I decided to live in Israel for a period of time in my early 20's. I tried learning French as well, but didn't have the same commitment to it due to a strong personality clash between myself and my teacher. When I left that school in Year 10, Mr Croissant and I said goodbye to each other with a smug "merci beaucoup shithead" and I never attempted it again.

On top of attending a Jewish school every Saturday for most of my teenage life, I went to a Jewish Youth Group called Habonim Dror which is a Jewish, Socialist-Zionist, youth movement that operates throughout Australia and around the world. The aim is to enrich the identities of the youth in the community, providing them with the ability to develop a meaningful Jewish identity that exists in all spheres of life. It certainly provided me with a link to my Jewish-ness but more so, it provided for me an external family and a social group I came to love and depend on.

I turned 17 in 1989 and, to my great pleasure and relief, I actually graduated from high school and received my VCE (Victorian Certificate of Education). I didn't make any plans to go straight to university or get a job as there was an opportunity to travel to Israel for a year with roughly 30 of my peers from the youth movement. It was an intensive 10 month educational and leadership program which provided us with an opportunity to understand, explore and experience the country and history of Israel, and also showed us how to live a Socialist-Zionistic life. Including all these culturally enhancing and soul evolving benefits, it was also a damn fine chance to get drunk and party with my friends in a foreign country with not much adult supervision. Now we're talking!

One of the requirements before travelling overseas was a physical check - to confirm I was fit and healthy for travel and living away from home. I went to my local Doctor and, in the midst of all the tests, I thought I'd fess up about some of the head hiccup symptoms I'd been experiencing in the mornings. It was a bold move on my part, as the results could have meant an end to my trip away, but I was clearly channelling the energy of 'Electro Girl' and feeling particularly brave and indestructible that morning. To my relief, the doctor just wrote it off, claiming I was getting out of bed too quickly and I should lie there for a while to let my mind wake up more before I got into the shower. Insert running man dance here!

Even though he told me what I wanted to hear, I'm still amazed at his lack of enquiry into my symptoms. If you know your stuff, you would know to delve a little deeper when a teenager is telling you about brain jerking and falling in the mornings; these aren't exactly everyday teenage behaviours. None of this mattered, though, as all I was focused on was going on an adventure to live in Israel and leaving Melbourne, the head hiccups, and the falling in the shower scenarios behind.

The majority of my time in Israel was spent on a Kibbutz with a crew of 14 of us, 10 boys and 4 girls and as we lived in a small space, we got to know each other quite well within a short space of time. A kibbutz, back in those days, was essentially a collective community, based on socialist ideals, where members work and share common wealth.

We all had daily jobs to do which we weren't paid for, as the philosophy of Kibbutz living was, at that time, that you are given accommodation and food in exchange for contributing to the running of the place. This concept is recognized internationally now and is referred to as WWOOFING (Willing Workers On Organic Farms). When we weren't on Kibbutz we were travelling around the country on tours that spanned from walking up Masada, tours across the desert, feeling the powerful energy in Jerusalem and being amongst it and we also spent a week learning what it would be like to be enlisted in the Israeli army, to the extent where I was taught how to load and shoot an M16 rifle. I was a lousy shot, but I looked pretty good in my camo gear!

From a young age, all I wanted was to be in a relationship. I was searching for the security and safety of being with a man who was going to take care of me (or at least this was my fantasy). I didn't get it from my dad during my teenage years when I needed it the most, so I was on the hunt for it now, ready to hang on tight at whatever cost.

My first experience was on the Kibbutz with one of the guys in my group. Derrick, my first "real" boyfriend. I was of the mindset that we were in it for the long haul and began looking to him for a sense of belonging; the two of us against the world kind of thing.

We were away from parents, we were young, we drank a shit load and had really awkward, bad, teenage sex which left me seriously wondering what the big deal was all about. I was living in the same room as Derrick, so he became accustomed to my head hiccups. They didn't happen all the time, but when they did, it would usually be in the mornings after a night of drinking. Within 10 minutes of being awake, I would feel flutters in my head, which would start quite lightly and then, depending on the situation, usually relating to lack of sleep, those flutters could turn into a stronger misfire within my brain, sort of like when you are sitting up and you start to fall asleep, your head drifts down and you suddenly wake up with a jolt. The stronger misfires would be the ones that would leave me needing to sit or lie down to avoid the inevitable dropping like a rag doll to the floor.

Another situation that brought them on was fights or heated discussions, and my brain would surge from the stress with electrical misfires that would come on quite strong during the argument but disappear quickly once the heated conversation was over. As I hadn't been diagnosed at this point, I didn't directly relate my emotional state to anything happening electrically in my brain and I was adamant it was all alcohol related and left it at that. I didn't talk more about it and Derrick didn't enquire. Life went on and we kept ignoring the symptoms. I think it just became accepted as one of my quirks and no one mentioned it.

Ignoring the symptoms was my way of avoiding dealing with it, but the crack was widening as I was living in close confines with people who were seeing them. Something had to give, and I remember very well the day I had a seizure in my bedroom on the Kibbutz and ended up falling through a glass table. It was the first time I had actually blacked out completely and had a 'Grand Mal' seizure since the symptoms started four years prior. A Grand Mal seizure features a loss of consciousness and intense muscle contractions. It's the type of seizure most people picture when they think about seizures in general. Apparently, I was thrashing about in the broken glass and when I became conscious of my surroundings (maybe 20 minutes later), I was lying in bed with the nurse in the room and everybody looking pretty freaked out.

Keep in mind; nobody knew anything at this stage. The nurse had asked my roommates if I had epilepsy, but obviously their reply was no, so nothing was followed up about it. The fact was, I was petrified of knowing what was happening to me and the feeling of being so disconnected from myself that I couldn't even remember falling through a glass table was haunting me, but I wasn't prepared to give up my lifestyle and miss out on all the fun. You'd think that experience would have made me want to look a bit deeper into it, but the decision was mine and I chose to continue on as if nothing was wrong. I was learning quickly that my fear of missing out (FOMO) was more powerful at this stage than my fear of finding out. The stronger, all-encompassing fear of missing out won.

My parents weren't notified and I saw the year out without having to miss out on anything socially, whilst at the same time, missing out dearly on the love and attention I desperately needed to give myself in order to address what was going on for me emotionally, mentally, chemically, physiologically and neurologically.

You teach people how to treat you by what you allow,
what you stop and what you reinforce.

Tony Gaskins

CHAPTER 3

The Jig is Up

I returned from my year away in Israel at the beginning of 1991 with no money, no job and no ambition, but I did have a few photo albums worth of priceless memories and about 10kgs worth of extra weight on my ass. To be honest, I didn't leave school with much ambition or fire in my belly to make a difference to the world, so I hadn't put much thought into what I was going to do now that I was finished school and I had to make a living. After pondering how to make my future millions for a few weeks, I decided I'd utilize my people skills to study and work in the hospitality industry. I liked alcohol, so naturally it made sense that I should become a bar chick and get paid to help others like alcohol, too. I signed up for a hospitality and tourism course not long after that epiphany and started working behind the bar at a hotel in the Melbourne CBD - where I learnt how to shake a cocktail *and* my booty to get some pretty good tips.

I was living back in the old family home with mum until I could afford to get a place of my own and move out. We had entered a new realm of living together, though. As I left Australia at 17 - just out of school, reliant on lifts everywhere, and underage; I came home from Israel, an 18 year old - able to drive, able to buy alcohol and cigarettes, and becoming more independent as I started to earn my own money. Suddenly that large house I grew up in became a lot smaller due to the secret I was still intent on hiding from her and the rest of the world. I was going out and having late nights, drinking, and getting stoned so I had to up the ante in order to hide the symptoms and Electro Girl started to become more of a functional presence for me. In my early teens when the symptoms started, those late nights and alcohol fuelled mornings were non-existent so the symptoms were happening less frequently and much easier to hide when they did occur.

I'll never forget that clear spring morning in September of 1991 - the day that mum witnessed me fall to the ground in front of her. We were in the kitchen discussing something that was getting both of us revved up. Then it happened, without any warning; my head misfired and I dropped to the ground. I remember it so clearly because I had never seen her look so confused and afraid before. She had no idea what she was witnessing and I remember the look of fear in her eyes that reflected what I had been fearing - the Jig was up! I tried to reassure her everything was alright, but between my brain misfiring, me falling to the ground, and trying to contain my own anxiety, even I was finding it hard to believe that I had it under control.

Somehow, I managed to sit her down and let her know that, as foreign as this looked to her, it wasn't foreign to me at all, and what I needed was for her to be calm so I could explain a few things. I couldn't hide it anymore; it was time to come clean with her. It was time for the Queen of Bullshit (me) to be dethroned – BUGGER. Shit was about to go down and I wasn't looking forward to any of it! Electro Girl must have been getting her Shellac nails refilled at that stage as she was nowhere to be found when this all went down and I had to take responsibility all on my own.

I intuitively believed mum probably knew something wasn't right years before, when she heard loud crashes in the shower - but she was having difficulties with her own emotional life at the time, trying to raise three daughters and deal with her divorce, plus I guess I made a pretty convincing case that everything was fine, so she hadn't pursued it.

There was no more room to move and, within minutes of telling her what was going on, plans were made to go straight to the doctor. Mum told him what she witnessed and then I told him my side of the story. I had to admit to both of them that this wasn't an isolated event and that this had been happening for the past four years. The doctor picked it straight away; the medical term for what I had was 'epilepsy'. "What the hell is epilepsy?" I thought, "Pffttt, whatever; this will be over in a couple of weeks." He had a real go at mum for not picking it up earlier and bringing me to him sooner. I had a real go at him for having a go at mum and reiterated that I'd hidden the symptoms from everyone for the last four years. He made me an appointment with a neurologist immediately and I was to have an MRI, CAT scan and an EEG ASAP. OMFG I was in acronym hell!

An EEG, for those who are unfamiliar, is a test that detects electrical activity in your brain using electrodes that are attached to your scalp with this gooey gross glue. I remember feeling intrigued and amused by it at the time, after all it was all a bit of a guessing game so I was joking around with the nurses and making light of the situation to help me get through the dread of thinking "What if it is this epilepsy shit they think it is?" Meanwhile they were asking me questions and holding up random images in front of me to trigger off certain electrical responses.

A week later, I went in for my first lot of CAT scans and another appointment was made to see the neurologist to discuss my results. I remember having to wait for about two hours to see the doctor. He was running late and I was feeling pretty anxious about our meeting, so having to wait longer just added to my overall frustration. There I was, sitting in his waiting room, looking at all the other anxious people waiting for their verdict from him, which would potentially change their existence forever, and I started to feel excruciatingly numb. My name was finally called and I walked into his office one type of person and walked out another type. He slapped the diagnosis of petit mal epilepsy on me. My seizures were tonic clonic/absence seizures and the treatment was to take 1000mg of Epilim a day. (When I reflect back on this initial diagnosis now, it is evident to me through my experiences what a guessing game this whole thing actually is, as this is not the current diagnosis I live with.)

"Bullshit," was my first response. We hadn't built up a rapport so I didn't trust him and I certainly didn't believe him when he said that I was going to be on medicine for the rest of my life. Then he told me if I had any questions about what we'd discussed, I should go to the Epilepsy Foundation who provide a great support network for people living with epilepsy and their friends and families, and they would answer all my questions. At that moment, I had lost my battle to deal with this on my own, and no matter how hard I tried to rebel against the decision, I began to take the tablets because now mum knew I was 'sick' and I was under her roof. I had no choice in the outcome, it seemed, and I could already hear my voice starting to fade in the system that was now all about diagnoses, doctors, and treatments.

Epilim was a nightmare for me. I found it to be a very bad 'solution' to treating my symptoms. The side effects were horrendous. I put on upwards of 15kg in less than six months, my hair was falling out in clumps and I started to get depressed. When I looked in the mirror, I hated what I saw. Not only was I fat and balding at the ripe old age of 19, but I despised the fact I had to succumb to taking medicine that was having such a massively negative effect on me. Bastards! The more I pushed my feelings away, the more depressed I would feel because I was ignoring the surging emotions underneath it all. All I wanted was to express to someone, and have them believe, that the seizures had a significant connection to my emotional health. No one seemed to want to give this concept any merit and unfortunately at that stage, I wasn't of the maturity or understanding to confidently back up my story as I was a newbie to the scene and didn't really know what epilepsy was anyway. The verdict was in and the diagnosis wasn't up for debate or discussion. Lucky for me, mum was open to getting a second opinion when she saw how distressed I had become due to the side effects!

My auntie knew of a doctor who was, and still is, one of the leading neurologists in Melbourne, and she arranged a consultation with him. I had another EEG and a CAT scan to see if I had any lesions, scars, or wounds on my brain causing the seizures, and blood and urine tests to check my medicinal levels and my kidneys. The results came back a week later and didn't really offer any satisfaction because they were inconclusive, or idiopathic if you want the medical lingo used. That is to say, there was no answer as to the exact type of epilepsy I was going to be branded with. Also, there was no exact medicine they could put me on in the interim, due to the tests being inconclusive.

The next step was to book me into the Austin Hospital in Melbourne to be monitored 24 hours a day for as long as it took to have a seizure, so they could record what was happening in my brain. I was put in a ward with other people who were there for similar reasons. They were all waiting patiently for their brains to have a massive glitch so that it was on record. I had the infamous gooey electrodes attached to my head again, and a turban type wrap around the electrodes so they didn't fall off. These electrodes were attached to an EEG machine, recording every electrical piece of information going on in my brain. I had a reclining chair, a television, a blanket and the Super Mario Brothers hooked up into my telly which was the number one video game at the time. The rest was up to my brain...

The lights needed to stay on 24/7, because the environment had to be as uncomfortable as possible in order to induce a seizure. I felt like a chicken in a battery farm, but I knew after one day of

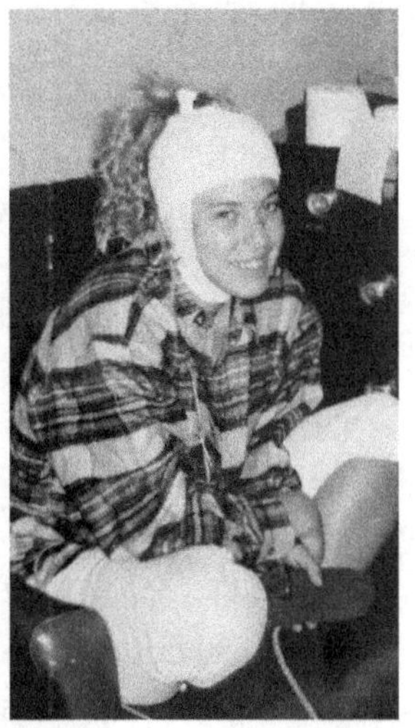

Me at the Austin hospital in 1994

being in that room, I wasn't going to simply have a seizure because the lights were on. Bring in the booze, bring in the party, bring in an ex-boyfriend to stir me up, *then* keep your bloody lights on and I'll show you a seizure!

I remember making friends with a girl called Claire. She was in the next room and was hooked up to the monitors with her amazing turban just like mine, waiting to have her great seizure debut. She had been in there a week already when I got there, so for her to finally get some company was like "winning the lotto". She was only about five years older than me and the first person I had ever met with epilepsy. I learned from her and her story that this condition could affect the rest of my life quite negatively. I hadn't thought about it like this before as I wasn't thinking long term about dealing with epilepsy; I had just figured it was something that could be cured. She mentioned her own experiences about not being able to drive because she had seizures, and people not hiring her because she was a potential risk, and that she had never had an intimate relationship with a man, and about the stigma associated with it in the outside world and suddenly it was all sounding really fucking unappealing for me to even associate with all these negatives - so I didn't.

I continued listening to her, fascinated but not afraid, as I didn't believe her experiences had anything to do with what I would have to go through. It simply wasn't on my radar to believe that if I had to live with having epilepsy, it would stop me doing anything I wanted to do. Among all these negative experiences Claire was relaying to me, I noticed one heart-warming quality about her that stood out to me as it was something I couldn't relate to in my journey with it thus far. When she spoke, there was peace and acceptance in her words. It was like she just knew her lot in life was doctors and hospitals and tests and she accepted it with grace. No fight, no lies, no kicking and screaming about the unpredictability of her brain, and no embarrassment. Were they qualities that I might have to embrace as well?

I had been in hospital five days and hadn't had a seizure. I was still hooked up to the machines though, as this was part of the deal until my head was read. I thought to ask the staff to bring an exercise bike to the room for me, so I could elevate my body temperature. That's one thing I remembered from my past that often had an effect on my electrical activity. Surprisingly, they obliged me with this and off I rode on an adventure to nowhere physically, but mentally, I was out of that room and on my way to Paris.

Whilst I was riding, I remember hearing this horrific noise from Claire's room and I'll never forget it because it sounded like gun shots being fired. There was a deep groaning noise and a clanging of metal and I remember feeling quite petrified. I had never heard anything like this before from another human being. I quickly grabbed the mobile monitor that I was hooked up to, wheeled it over to the door and, for the first time ever, I witnessed someone having a Grand Mal seizure. The nurses were holding her down and she was making deep moaning noises whilst the metal sides of the hospital bed were clanging about due to her convulsions shaking the foundations of the bed. The staff wouldn't let me watch, so I remember having to hear the rest of her seizure from my room - in a foetal position, scared shitless.

Sure enough, I had a seizure that evening. Whether it was from the exercise bike or the shock of seeing and hearing Claire have a super Grand Mal seizure, I'll never know, but I was bloody glad I had one because it meant I would finally be able to get out of that hospital room.

This was and still is the only time I have seen someone have a seizure in person. That day changed something in me forever and had a huge effect on me. I knew how I felt looking at her, so helpless and vulnerable, hearing the noises she was making, and I knew right then and there that I didn't want anyone to see me like that, ever, out of fear they might be scared of me and reject me.

After my seizure, the results came through and I left the hospital with a diagnosis of tonic clonic epilepsy. I was put on an anti-convulsant called Tegretol for a period of time just on its own and then Rivotril, another anti-convulsant, was added a few months later since I apparently needed not just one, but a cocktail of meds to stop the symptoms. I was living a doped up existence on a visual palette of anti-convulsants and over a short period of time, the medicines were starting to take over my life and moods. My trust in the system was starting to decline, fuelled more and more by feeling like a human experiment rather than an individual case. I surrendered to it at that stage, all the while knowing deep down there had to be a reason for my seizures and a better way of healing than all these meds and side effects. After all, I wasn't born with the symptoms and nobody could prove to me that it was genetic and therefore irreversible.

It was at this stage I reached a pivotal point in my evolution. I was 20, had just been handed my epilepsy sentence and I had two options as I saw it. I could settle down in Melbourne and take things easy for a while, whilst I explored my seizures and ways to manage it through other modalities than the medical system, or I could go off on another adventure to Israel, still slightly unstable and in denial.

I chose denial. I convinced myself that my life was so much better when I lived in Israel so I decided to pack up and move back there, far away from doctors, diagnoses and treatments.

Never do anything by halves if you want to get away with it. Be outrageous. Go the whole hog. Make sure everything you do is so completely crazy it's unbelievable...

Roald Dahl

CHAPTER 4

Young and Invincible

On the 6th of July 1992, Electro Girl and I left Australia and arrived in Israel 24 hours later. I had booked myself on to a kibbutz before I left Australia for six months to do an Ulpan (oolpun) which is designed to teach participants the basic Hebrew language skills of conversation, writing and comprehension in a classroom situation, as well as being required to work for the kibbutz community in return for allowing us to stay there. Approximately 60 people from all over the world were doing the program and not one of them knew that I had a 'problem'. I was still pretty overweight from the side effects of the medicine I was on, still branded an epileptic by the medical profession, but to these people I was living with, I was just another new face to get to know.

When I first got there, a girl I knew from New Zealand was expecting me and had therefore saved me a space in her room along with another girl from England. We were to be assigned classes, work schedules, made aware of the kibbutz rules and, of course, when and where the parties were going to be held. My roommates knew about my condition, and in the beginning they witnessed the head hiccups but nothing more severe. They were really supportive and never made me feel bad about my choices, but I don't think they fully understood why I kept drinking alcohol and staying up late seeing that they were triggers for me. I hadn't introduced them to Electro Girl at that stage.

I started working in the dining room, the most boring place of all to work. On a kibbutz, the dining hall was run a little like a buffet/

cafeteria. There was no set menu and no individual ordering, just islands of food from which you were served from someone behind a buffet as well as some self serve areas. There were piles of trays, plates, and cutlery and you just found a place in the line and went for it. My job description was to top up the food displays so that there was always enough, and to remove all the dirty crockery and cutlery to the kitchen for some other unlucky bastard who had to wash them, dry them and put them away. Needless to say I didn't last there very long, and quickly switched over to working in the garden amongst nature, in the sunlight.

One Sunday night, after a weekend of dancing, drinking and lack of sleep (a cocktail of *unawesome* for me) I made my way to the dining hall at dinnertime, in order to line my stomach with some much needed food. There would have been 300 people living on this kibbutz at the time, but not all ate communally at every meal. That night it was particularly busy and there were perhaps 300 people waiting in line to make their way through the many choices of food for dinner. I was standing there with my tray full of food waiting for the desert line to start moving when all of a sudden I started getting the head hiccups. As usual, I chose to ignore them because I thought they would go away, I hoped and prayed they would go away, actually. To my dismay, they were there to stay and play and within moments, one head hiccup ended in me losing control of the brain connection to my arms and I dropped my tray of food all over the floor. The outcome was a horrendously loud crash of broken plates smashing on the floor and cutlery ricocheting off the stainless steel bain maries. Luckily no one was hurt and it didn't morph into a Grand Mal seizure.

I remember through the haze that I was escorted away from hundreds of staring eyes by a man I had never seen before. I tried to explain to everyone that I had had too much sun on the weekend and this was just a bit of sunstroke (that was actually a new excuse I was trying out to see how believable it was, but clearly it was taking it to a new level of bullshit), but this man Benny seemed to know exactly what was going on.

He was a member of the kibbutz and found it in his heart to come with me to the kibbutz doctor and stay until I was all right. He didn't play a big part in the grand scheme of things but the role he played, he played with love and compassion for a stranger, which I very much needed at the time.

The doctor on the kibbutz got to know me quite well from that day on and for whatever reason, be it pity, compassion, or just because she grew to like me, she wanted to help. She became a surrogate mother at the time and she genuinely cared about my welfare above and beyond her role. I sat in her office and spilled my guts to her about everything and she got me an appointment with a neurologist so that my medicine could be monitored and changed. Yay!!! I may not have been able to get off the meds, but I could perhaps find a drug that had less side effects and didn't make me feel like a fat zombie.

The neurologist I had been booked to see was a Russian man who spoke Hebrew and Russian, but didn't speak a word of English. As the only word I knew how to say in Russian at the time was spasiba (thankyou) and my Hebrew was still pretty rusty, I took with me my kibbutz "dad" as an interpreter. Everyone on the Ulpan or who is volunteering is assigned a "family" for their time on the kibbutz. I was really lucky and was allocated to a fabulous couple. I used to hang out with them a lot. Steve, my "dad", eventually became my boss, too, as he signed me up to start working on the dairy farm with him, milking over 200 cows and looking after the new born calves. The hours were sometimes a bit hard to fathom but a 4am milking meant I could be on the private beach of the kibbutz by 12.30pm, with the whole rest of the day up my sleeve.

I had so many blood tests in the following three months that I was seriously starting to feel a bit like a pin cushion, but my meds were changed and I was satisfied. By this stage the Ulpan was about to end and I wanted to continue volunteering, I really didn't want to leave this bubble where, even though I was still nowhere near stable health wise, I felt safe and unjudged about the seizures and the epilepsy, even if there were plenty of judgements about the way I chose to live my life.

Accepting volunteers is normally an easy decision for the assigned board of directors of the kibbutz, as they need the help where they can get it. It's very rare that they refuse the help but, in my case, it had to be taken to a vote by all the members of the kibbutz, not just the board. The reason for this was that I came with a history of an illness and I had proved to be a bit of a handful. Luckily, I had a lot of people rooting for me to stay because they liked me, and so the vote went in my favour. I stayed on as a volunteer and continued working in the dairy farm for the next five months.

One morning in particular, I remember very well. I had to get up for a four o'clock milking and I had only gotten to bed at one in the morning. On this occasion, I rode my bike to work instead of walking because I was late. I was frantically pedalling and then out of nowhere had a strong cranial misfire and before I knew it, I had hit my head on the handle bars, bounced off them, and landed teeth first on the bitumen road. I could taste blood but all I could think about was being late for work and not wanting anyone at work to know that it was because of the epilepsy. I picked myself up off the ground and wheeled the bike to work, limping in agony with a grazed leg. I was pretty messy, as you can imagine. I had completely knocked out my two front teeth and there was blood and gravel all over my face. My first job when I arrived at work was to wipe away the blood, clean off the road rash and then go and round up the cows. I managed to hide from the guy who I was working with at the start of my shift, he knew I was there getting the cows but hadn't seen me. I thought that by the time I got the cows into the milking corral, the misfiring would have stopped.

I went out to round up one lot of cows, probably about 100 of them, and the head hiccups and adjoining electrical jolts were coming on hard and fast. I'd walk a few steps, have a few brain jolts, try and not lose my footing but when I did, I'd fall into an endless field of fresh cow shit. Then again, walk a few steps, and fall in the shit. The cows at this stage usually know the drill, they do it twice a day every day with no holidays or sick days so it's pretty second nature to them; human comes to herd cows, cows move towards the milking station. That day however, they knew something was not right and they stopped herding and just stood there looking at my get up/fall down show and formed a circle around me and started 'mooing' at me. They weren't going anywhere and from my position lying on the ground in their shit watching their confused, inquisitive faces, I finally started to question what the fuck I was doing. Electro Girl flew in at this stage and helped me sort out this mess.

I managed to pull myself together and move them, but I got into the milking station very fragile, still misfiring, limping, covered in cow shit from head to toe and bleeding from my mouth still as I hadn't addressed the wounds from the fall at that stage. The guy I was working with took one look at me with a mixture of compassion and pity in his eyes and sent me home. I had no front teeth for about two weeks before I went to go and get dental work done to cap my two front teeth. The massive lesson was learned and it was definitely the associated physical pain involved that made me promise to never put myself in a situation like that again.

I left the kibbutz eventually and moved to Tel Aviv for another crazy 12 months in Israel still creating situations that put my health at risk and convincing myself that I was ok. I lived with a couple of guys for a period of time and when I got in touch with one of them, Zvi, recently to tell him about my book, he mentioned that the only regret he has about that incredible time we were living together was not addressing the "elephant in the room" with me. In this case, the elephant wasn't the sagging tattoo on my breast, it was the seizures and their related triggers. They happened, I lived with them, people around me lived with them but no one really talked about them because I built up such a wall of resistance around myself and the topic that no one dared bring it up. I sound scary but I was harmless. It was all created from my survival instinct, my "flight" response, to avoid dealing with the emotional issues behind the seizures and in this magical, illusionary world of avoidance, I was invincible.

He who cures a disease may be the skillfullest, but he that prevents it is the safest physician.

Thomas Fuller

CHAPTER 5

When Sparks Fly

Now would be a good time to talk about what epilepsy is. Epilepsy, or seizure disorders, are one of the oldest recorded afflictions of humankind. According to a recent document from WHO (World Health Organisation) approximately 50 million people worldwide have epilepsy, making it one of the most common neurological diseases globally.

Before I knew what epilepsy was, I only associated the word with people having weird spasms and freaky fits. It is a common misconception and to a large degree, what creates a scary stigma for people is that epilepsy always involves violent convulsions and visibly obvious seizures where someone falls to the ground and starts shaking. In fact there are around 40 different types of epilepsy and epilepsy syndromes with one common symptom - seizures - that disrupt the normal activity of the central nervous system. Seizures are not a disease, they are a symptom of dozens of different disorders that can affect the brain. Some seizures can hardly be noticed, while others, Grand Mal's, are totally disabling.

When people are nervous and feeling afraid, vulnerable or pressured, a range of symptoms can be experienced. Some people get butterflies in their tummies, some people have heart palpitations or panic attacks, some people don't feel a thing and have no reaction. Some experience the ingrained fight or flight response intensely, some need to release bowels and bladder and then some people, like me, with a low seizure threshold, drop to the ground and have a Grand Mal seizure.

Everyone is born with a 'seizure threshold', which is medical jargon meaning the level of neurological stimulation capable of precipitating a seizure. My understanding of this is, every person has an inbuilt system that controls the excitory and inhibitory forces in their brain. In "normal" brains the GABA (inhibitory neurotransmitter) and Glutamate (excitory neurotransmitter). These types of brains have a high seizure threshold and are less likely to have any electrical overload, because of all the safeguards working against having one

Neurotransmitters such as GABA and Glutamate play a very important role in the equilibrium and functioning of our brains. GABA is the one keeping us relaxed, chilled, sedated, the one that fuels the parasympathetic nervous system and in some people, GABA production may not be as high as the Glutamate (the excitory one). Therefore, when there are enormous amounts of electrical activity going on in your synapses, GABA is what would normally be called on to calm the storm. This way the brain remains homeostatically balanced and electrically stable, which in turn makes the person upright and functional, as a rule of thumb. I, unfortunately, either don't produce enough on my own or my brain just doesn't use it properly.

If your brain is wired in such a way that you have a low seizure threshold, meaning that the amounts of GABA and glutamate in your system can't balance each other out naturally, you will be more prone to sensitivities and triggers around you which lowers your threshold for protection against your brain sparking. This is more common than you think it is! These triggers can be things like drinking alcohol, sleep deprivation, stress, illness, tumours, brain injuries, flickering lights and menstruation or hormonal imbalances to name just a few. Being an epileptic is, in itself, a major source of stress. There is the constant uncertainty of not knowing when or where the next episode will occur. Even normal interactions with well-meaning friends, workmates, or family members can often transform negatively once they witness an epileptic seizure.

Attempts to treat epileptic seizures date back to medieval times where sufferers were thought to be possessed by evil spirits which had to be removed. The methods used at the time included: drilling a hole in the skull of the patient, flagellation, applying leeches to the face, and practicing exorcism to drive the demons out of the brain. (1) Harsh, right! From there, we move to the time before Hippocrates, when the "sacred disease" was thought to be an illness sent by the gods, people would offer sacrifices and take part in religious acts under the instruction of a doctor-priest in an attempt to be cured. The supporters of Hippocratic medicine, who believed that epilepsy had a natural cause and tried to treat the disease using natural means. The treatment was based on dietetics, or a structured, "sensible" lifestyle.

When I was diagnosed, all the well-known treatments were of a very pharmaceutical nature which didn't include any skull drilling thankfully and I found very little back then on dealing with diet, emotions, or hormones as an avenue to treatment. You were just labelled an epileptic and the displayed symptoms needed to be dealt with. Sure, lifestyle choices were taken into consideration like enough sleep, no alcohol, and eliminating stress, but it was a very black and white treatment plan. The medical world only treated tangible things like symptoms. The intangible things like psychology, emotions and hormones were not considered important to the treatment and diagnosis. You were handed a "magic pill" and monitored to make sure your symptoms, not the underlying issue causing the symptoms, had been treated. Thankfully the days have passed since diagnosed epileptics were burnt at the stake and thought to be devil spawn, as that would have really looked bad on my current resume.

We have an innate need inside us to fix and help people and, as friends and onlookers find out, there is nothing you can do for a person having a Grand Mal seizure except relax, smile, be present and give time aside to seeing the situation through with the person. As I mention to my onlookers, most importantly just make sure that something soft is under my face so that it isn't rubbing on the ground or I will come out with concrete burns, carpet burns, or even grass stains depending on where my head ends up at the time.

So how does living with epilepsy feel for me? Hmm, well - let's continue the journey through the epi-porthole of my life.

A couple of months after I was diagnosed and put on medication to treat the symptoms, an opportunity arose to move out of mum's house and into a share house with two school mates. I was stabilised on the medication and was having no symptoms or seizures so I figured it was a good time to crawl out of the secure nest I was living in and start to fend for myself. I lived with the boys for one year, and during that time I started seeing a guy called Dylan who was the younger brother of one of the guys I had moved in with.

Dylan intrigued me from the moment I saw him because he was a bit of a rebel, gothic looking misfit which for some reason was sexy to me at the time. He seemed to tick all my misinformed boxes as far as good long term relationship fodder. He was younger, not very confident, and he seemed to have more issues than me, so I could potentially "save" him and he would never leave me because he would need me too much. Tragic, huh? This scenario reeks of abandonment issues!

We were in the love bubble for a while, and he was infatuated by the sky and the universe and so we spent many nights gazing through his telescope and pondering space. It was a wonderful place to get lost, as it was so far away from the reality I was living, so gazing upwards and contemplating other worlds was a welcome relief. He also had his motorbike license and a powerful Honda 1200CC bike which was a big tick from my side of things, and I just loved riding on the back of his bike with the wind wrapping around me, and feeling so close to everything that was zooming by. He loved camping as well, so we'd go off into nature and explore. Things were looking positive for us in the bubble, so I decided to move out of the share house and into a place with him. I was still experiencing side effects from the medications like drowsiness and emotional highs and lows, but the seizures seemed a thing of the past and a brighter future was seemingly imminent.

I had started to move my sights from a career in the hospitality industry to a career working with animals. Working in the hospitality industry had turned me off working with humans for a while, so off I went to prove myself in the animal world. Over a seven year period I became an Animal Technician and then got my qualifications as a Veterinary nurse. This brought an immense amount of joy into my world and I couldn't see myself ever working outside of this industry. I was going to build my way up to working with wildlife in national parks and one day even going to work in elephant orphanages in Africa. I was actually becoming ambitious!

Moving in with someone will always be the make or break for a relationship. Not long after we moved in together, I started to understand that Dylan was going to be harder work than I'd anticipated. He started to display signs of jealousy if I spent time with anyone else and he had anger issues, which I didn't witness before we moved in, that would often turn up out of the blue. Over the years, a lot of my possessions ended up smashed or broken in many of his anger fuelled outbursts. An incident springs to mind of one night when we'd had a massive argument and in the middle of it he hopped on his motorbike to go for a ride. He was inconsolable before he got on the bike, and I knew it was not going to end well. I actually thought that I'd be getting a phone call from the morgue asking me to come and identify his body. Hours went by and I hadn't heard from him and I was beside myself with worry. In the wee hours of the morning I received a call from the Albury police (which was a three hour ride from where we lived) to let me know that he was alive, but that he was being detained, as he was in a high speed chase along the Hume Highway for miles and had been clocked at speeds of 240km/hr in a 100km/hr zone. He needed to be bailed out and would have to appear in court, facing charges of dangerous riding and running from the cops. A sentence would see him put away for eight months and during the long process of appeals and waiting for hearings etc. that spanned out over one and a half years, he sank into an even bigger pit of doom and gloom.

I was so committed to protecting my wounded inner child from feeling abandoned that I completely dismissed all logic and reason that told me I needed to leave him. Dylan grew even more socially awkward and built a brick wall around himself which made it hard for people to connect with him at all. People would try to be friendly but he was an angry young man with a bad attitude. My outgoing personality got totally trampled underneath the relationship, but the martyr in me was going to save him, goddammit! I wanted the relationship to work so badly that I even agreed to marry him when he asked thinking the relationship would get better if we were married. My main focus was for us to not end up divorced like my parents, as this was the ultimate failure in my eyes, so I kept trying to flog a dead horse and keep this abusive relationship alive, albeit very unhappily.

My saving grace at the time was the wacky weed. Dylan and I were habitual marijuana smokers and we hung out at home stoned a lot. Smoking pot was really good at numbing my emotional pain. I was taking medicines that were making me fat and bald, my self-confidence was shredded, and I was with a boy who hated the world and most people, and his obsession with watching late night porn made our love life extremely monotone as he was getting the fix he needed on the screen.

As much as I love to blame the meds for my weight gain, I'm sure that some of my weight issues could have also been attributed to the fact that I had the munchies for seven years. My daily routine was: work, eat, smoke, pass out on couch, wake up, work, eat, smoke, eat, go to bed. On top of the side effects of the medicines, the head hiccups were back and the weed was casting a dark cloud over me too, so any chance of shining any light on this situation in order to extract myself from it was becoming extremely low.

It was over this time that I decided to do my own research into epilepsy and was starting to connect some dots with the head hiccups and my stress levels, and starting to make some definitive connections between my emotional/mental state and the seizures. I had more insight into how love and emotions were actually a huge part of what triggers my seizures and for all the drama that was our situation, Dylan was assisting me to work this out, simply through allowing me to observe myself in our tumultuous relationship.

The defining moment in our relationship (as well as the relationship between myself and the seizures) happened after about six years of being together. It was our first meeting with a counsellor to see if we could work out our issues. I was quite anxious about it but I was so good at hiding my feelings by then that I wasn't listening to my head giving me clear signals that some shit was about to go down. I had left work late, totally anxious, and I knew Dylan was going to freak out about my tardiness, so I got more anxious and of course at that stage I hadn't succumbed to owning a mobile phone, so I couldn't get in contact with him to let him know. The inner turmoil was rising and I was driving and not heeding the signs and bang... I hit the car in front of me during a seizure. Bad situation, not a bad smash because I wasn't going fast, but it certainly changed my attitude towards listening to myself and knowing the triggers and signs, which are so obvious, if I want to avoid a seizure.

An ambulance was called and I had to hand my license in until the doctor was satisfied I was seizure free and not a danger on the roads, which at the time was six months. Things surely weren't looking up for me, but family and friends who had been watching my relationship nightmare unfold over the years were pretty happy that I was off the road. I disappeared from the lives of some very close friends during this time without explaining why and hurt people in the process as they couldn't understand what was going on with me. I didn't know how to reach out for their help so hiding from them seemed like a much easier choice. I had trained myself to hide from people to avoid scaring them away. I thought I could do it on my own but I was failing miserably.

I ended my seven year relationship with Dylan not long after that (1999), and thankfully I learned a lot of positive, life changing stuff from the relationship. The most important lesson was this, and I'm going to use a metaphor. We all love skinny jeans, we wear them in order to hold in all our flaws and give the illusion that they fit perfectly. However, if you don't fit in to skinny jeans well and your stomach is hanging over the top and they just feel too tight and like your kidneys are going to pop out of your mouth, the best thing to do is wear something that compliments you better. There's got to be a better cut of jean for you. This is the lesson I learned with Dylan, he was my skinny jeans that just didn't fit me right, but I kept trying to force myself into them because I really wanted to believe I could look good in them. Thankfully the force of the uncomfortable tight fit split the whole relationship apart right down the mid seam.

The minute that relationship ended, I felt the fire rise in my belly to really succeed in addressing my pharmaceutical situation that I hated so much. It was only then that I started to feel confident that I could take on the system; that I had the power within me to heal myself and that there had to be other alternatives to the medications and the side effects. Even through the haze of the side effects, it was clear I needed to take myself off the meds and stop smoking pot in order to understand exactly where in my brain these triggers were stored and what sparked them. I am definitely not endorsing this as a solution as everyone is different and a big decision like this should always be discussed with your health professional. My neurologist at the time strongly advised against it but I was adamant that I needed to try it my way. So I packed my life up in Melbourne in 2000, extracted myself from the animal industry and headed straight for the "hippie hills" in northern New South Wales in an old beat up Kombi to try and find like minded people who might be able to assist me in a more natural approach to my life and my healing.

The key to any successful medical treatment is to define the underlying cause and neutralize it with natural remedies. This concept has eluded allopathic or traditional medicine and is the primary reason why the "sick" care system is failing miserably.

Gerald H. Smith

CHAPTER 6

An Alternative Pathway

Leaving Melbourne on an unknown adventure was exactly what my mind, body and soul needed after such a tumultuous decade. It was time to breathe in the fresh air and leave the city behind, so I could heal some wounds and start to feel the air beneath my bingo wings. My older sister Nicki, came on the initial 2000km drive from Melbourne to Byron Bay to make sure my cheap Kombi got me to my destination safely. She had been in a major car accident only a week before, but her body was healthy enough at the time to make the trek, so we took advantage of the fact that she was taking time off work due to the accident and drove off for some road trip fun.

The Kombi wasn't exactly a stand out example of the safest vehicle on the road, and she was pretty ugly to look at, but oh how I loved her. She represented freedom. The type of freedom that needed to be jump started every now and then, due to a low charging battery, but freedom nonetheless. We stopped along the way and visited nice beaches, country pubs, and road stops when we felt like we needed a rest. At one of the stops, we were sitting having a cuppa and two boys approached and started talking to us. They seemed really nice and wanted to look in my van at how I'd set it up to live in. We were cool, we were hip, and we were on the road, not a care in the world, peace to all. They peeked inside, had a look around and then, out of nowhere, grabbed my sister's bag with the intention of running with it. But it got caught on the door, which gave me a chance to stop them in their tracks. I pounced on the guy with the bag, pinned him to the ground and grabbed it back. They freaked out, took off running, and we went back to casually sipping our tea keeping a relaxed demeanour on the outside all the while on the inside a rush of pounding adrenaline was surging through our chests. We looked at each other, threw the cups and chairs in the back of the van, and then got the hell out of there pronto.

Our road trip was the last time Nicki really ever had full use of her body without ongoing trauma and pain. When she returned to Melbourne the fused discs in her lower back from the car accident needed intense rehab and eventually surgery, twice, so it was a memorable journey on many levels for us.

I was left to my own devices and was finally on my own. I felt completely safe as Electro Girl was in tow but I still had the mantra in my head that I needed to be in a relationship in order to feel complete. I stumbled across Jez within a few weeks of being on the road and he filled this role nicely for me. The attraction was immediate. My heart would race whenever I bumped into him in the street, and within a few months I moved in with him. He was the son of a gazillionaire and daddy had bought him a house in the hills on the Northern Rivers in Northern NSW. It was a massive property, where he lived with his crazy ex-partner, whenever she was in the neighbourhood, and their daughter.

I shared with him the story of where I'd come from and my history with epilepsy, and he passionately encouraged me to get off the meds because he believed I could beat it with alternative therapies and plant medicine. That was like music to my ears, because no one else had ever believed I could heal myself without the use of pharmaceuticals before. At this stage, it was a foreign concept to trust in my intuition, but I was willing to learn what I could and potentially risk my life in order to get off the medications, if it meant I might find seizure control through other means.

His place was like a rehab clinic for me in the beginning. In his little hideaway in the hills, I started to wean myself, ever so slowly, off the Tegratol and Rivotril cocktail I had been on for the last five years - which came with its pros and cons. I was very fragile coming off seven years of medications and also being outside of my comfort zone, so I had quite a few seizures during that time and my brain was highly, electrically unstable. He probably could have used me as an extra energy source and plugged the toaster, the telly, and the blender into various orifices for usage, but the topic was never brought up.

In order to balance out the physical and chemical detoxing I was undergoing, he also introduced me to Kinesiology, Hypnotherapy, and Crystal Healing in the hope that, emotionally, I would be able to cope better with the changes. Crystals have many healing qualities I found out at the time. Each variety of crystal has a unique internal structure, which causes it to resonate at a certain frequency that provides healing. I threw myself into this modality of healing fully. I loved the energy of crystals, the beauty, the texture, the concept, and the emotional safety I would feel just by having them around. They were in my bathroom, my van, my kitchen, my bedroom, on my fingers, my neck, absolutely everywhere, I even looked into getting a crystal vibrator but couldn't afford it at the time. It has been said that you don't find the crystal, the crystal finds you, thus I'm still patiently waiting for that crystal vibrator to find me. Yoo Hoo over here! Everyone is different but the crystals I found very useful for my electrical imbalances and emotions associated with the epilepsy, were Amethyst, Rose Quartz, Turquoise and Black Tourmaline.

Jez also took me to a health shop every now and then called Happy High Herbs (now known as the Happy Herb Company) which was like this mecca of plant medicines that I had never been exposed to before. They had remedies for all kinds of ailments and addictions in their natural form, straight from the plant and not in pills or capsules. He would take me there to get me to try some herbs for anxiety, relaxation and mood stabilization which was very necessary to balance me out whilst I was coming off the pharmaceutical medicines. I drank a lot of tea in that time, and the herbs really had a positive effect on me. I really liked and trusted this guy and wanted to impress on him and myself that I was tough and I could do this.

The epilepsy had appeared in my teenage years and I was now 29. I had shut down my emotions for so long about it so delving into the reasons behind it was inevitably about to become a long and arduous task, but I was getting off the medications, so I was up for the challenge because I was doing it my way. I decided to start with a session of hypnotherapy to see if I could delve into my deeper consciousness of pain. I thought, if people can stop smoking after one hour of hypnotherapy, why the hell wouldn't it cure me of my seizures, so I gave it a go. To be honest, I thought, if these blockages can be attended to with as little work from me as possible, I'm all for it! Of course, it didn't quite work as I had fantasized because I still kept having seizures. Needless to say, I never saw her again, not because I thought she was full of shit or anything, but because I had an unrealistic expectation that I was going to leave there seizure free and I didn't!

One other life changing decision came into play as well around this time with Jez. I was in my reproductive prime and very fertile. I had to make the call on two occasions with Jez to terminate pregnancies and convince myself that it was for the greater good of all. Due to the instability in my brain and my commitment to healing the seizures naturally, I made a very clear and confronting decision to never have children and instead to devote that time to myself and my own healing, and everything I was going to open myself up to along the way. To me, it was a no brainer. I didn't want to potentially pass this gene on to anyone else for them to suffer as I was, so on one hand, it was an easy decision to make. The fact was, being unstable and flopping to the ground from a misfiring brain was scary enough as it was, but I was only hurting myself in the process. If something were to happen to an unborn child during one of the falls, it could have been a fucking disaster to the future for both myself and the unborn child! The flip side was, the pregnancy may have been perfect and the gene not handed on and at times I think about the what ifs, but choices are choices and we make them for a reason. Lots of emotional turmoil was involved in this great love with Jez, which lasted for about two and a half intense years. At the end of it, he went back to his crazy ex-partner and Electro Girl took the reins, threw our stuff in the Kombi and led us straight to the Happy Herb Shop to learn as much as we could about their brain herbs.

The Happy Herb Company was born when Ray Thorpe and his best friend and business partner, Eliza, realised that natural herbs can have significant positive effects on both health and mood. Through research and experimentation, Ray discovered that herbs in their natural form can offer a safer, healthier, non-addictive alternative to many known medicinal and recreational drugs on the market. I couldn't have wished for better teachers than Ray and Eliza, for what I needed at the time and still to this day. I was a completely open book when I found them. As much as I loved living in the van, I was still having seizures and I knew I needed to find a place to live that wasn't on four wheels, especially since I was recently off all meds, suffering from a broken heart, and more determined than ever to continue searching for natural remedies for my seizures.

I entered their herb shop, which was situated in the main street of Nimbin (a well known hippie town in Northern NSW), to look around at different herbs for health and also to try and make some connections for a place to stay. They both happened to be in the shop that day which they mentioned was quite rare and I walked in and asked them if they knew anywhere I could park my van for a while in order to lick my metaphorical wounds. They looked at each other and asked "Do you like animals by any chance?"

Their home was an amazing wonderland of flora, fauna, colour, and artistic flair, and an immense amount of love had been put into building every square inch. In 2003, it became my paradise, where I had my own little self-contained cottage on the property and could come and go as I pleased. I did approximately six hours a week working on the mail orders for the business, which at that stage, had two shops and now has 30. I also looked after their property and all the animals when they went on the road to sell the herbs at festivals and expos. The menagerie of animals included chooks, peacocks, geese, two ostriches, horses, goats, dogs and cats. In exchange for this, I was allowed to stay in my little cottage, rent and bill free. It was a perfect deal for all parties and I loved being around them and their land. They became my extended family, my employers, and my friends for life. There have been many angels in my life who have come to my aid and looked out for me along the way, but these two have consistently been there through thick and thin. They gave me hope, a home, a herbal education, a job, moral support, and a new lease on life.

I was willing to try anything and everything outside the western medicine approach to treatment. I was just happy there was another way, where pharmaceuticals didn't have to take precedence. I was living a super optimistic existence, thinking there would be a magic herb or herbs that would be the exact medicine I needed. I fantasized about this outcome and being able to lift my middle finger to the world and scream, "Fuck you all, I told you so!"

I had access to a wide range of herbs used to optimise brain function. Herbs like Brahmi, Gotu Kola and Gingko for focus, clarity and memory. The seizures and meds do affect memory and clarity, and those herbs did wonders to assist in repairing that. Also, herbs like Scullcap, Catnip, and Blue Lily for relaxing the nervous system in order to calm my overactive brain. Of course the wonder herb Damiana was a saviour and still is. It is a mood stabiliser and was excellent in keeping me optimistic, which was a state so easy to lose amongst the electricity bursts. These outcomes are exactly what the pharmaceuticals are designed to do but herbs are unadulterated, milder on the system, and generally have no side effects. (This theory of course, can only be tested and trialled if more money is given to research herbal medicines through clinical trials into their medicinal effects, which it isn't. Unfortunately, it's siphoned back into the pharmaceutical industry to pump out more drugs in order to treat symptoms).

I started drinking these medicinal herbs as teas and incorporating them into my daily life. At the time I was really hoping taking herbs instead of pharmaceuticals was the sole answer I was looking for; it would be a simple transition and I'd be cured. The herbs worked wonders on many health levels for me. My skin was better and my kidneys and liver were improving after being compromised by so many years on medicines but, frustratingly, I was still having seizures. This didn't put me off though, it simply increased my hunger to seek out alternative therapies and medicines whilst still using the herbs.

I tried so many different healing modalities over the years like Bowen Therapy, Reiki, Acupuncture, Kinesiology, Restorative Yoga and I nearly even went and got my anal region probed and my colon cleansed with coffee; more so for the enjoyment factor than the thought that I'd be seizure free after. I never gave meditation a real crack at this point; I tried but just couldn't be bothered to be honest! It seemed too hard and took up too much time, and I had no focus. I wanted someone to heal me and I didn't want it to be me, so with this in mind, meditation was totally not the answer! I just wanted to keep living this "awesome" life and for others to heal me so I could just continue on spreading love and laughter into the world.

I spent four years in Northern NSW, topping up my knowledge bank with healthier approaches to life and, by 2004, I felt strong enough to return to Melbourne, off the meds and armed with a tool kit of healing modalities and herbs that would address and manage the seizures. I was returning to an unknown, though, as I knew there would be people who cared about me who would question why I was going down the alternative therapy path if I was still having seizures. I was hoping they would just accept and support why I was choosing this path and not question it. At the end of the day, there were a few who weren't pleased with my choices and really struggled with my stubbornness to remain off medications, but I didn't lose sleep, family or friends over it so the next challenge I faced was maintaining and building on this alternative healing knowledge back in the city.

Illusions commend themselves to us because they save us pain and allow us to enjoy pleasure instead. We must therefore accept it without complaint when they sometimes collide with a bit of reality against which they are dashed to pieces.

Sigmund Freud

CHAPTER 7

A Grand Mal Marriage

Melbourne is well known amongst locals and travellers for its array of live music, culture, entertainment, fine dining, and bars. I will always regard this city as home no matter where I live, which is a great thing, as I find myself drawn back to the allure of living amongst the excitement and variety of this glorious city every now and then. The year was 2004 and I was still off all meds; still having head hic-cups and seizures here and there, but I was generally living a very healthy lifestyle and becoming more in tune with the flow of my brain and body. I had been doing a bit of research on the association between diet, the health of our gut, and seizures when I came across the Ketogenic diet. The name Ketogenic means the diet produces ketones in the body (keto = ketone, genic = producing). Ketones are formed when the body uses fat as its source of energy instead of carbs converted to sugar. The Ketogenic diet is an effective seizure management modality for some but it is designed to be very high in fat and low in carbohydrates which doesn't work for everyone. With higher ketone levels, ie. more fat stores to gain energy from, this can often lead to improved seizure control. Initially, it interested me as a possible solution to the seizures, but as soon as I found out the diet was high in fats I immediately associated it with the possibility that weight gain was more than likely to occur and I kicked that idea straight to the curb. I suddenly felt a warm fuzzy comfort with the idea of having seizures, over looking like a beached whale.

Another dietary solution I stumbled across at the time was the modified Atkins diet, which had only just entered the realm of the health industry as a possible treatment for seizure control. The first paper on the success of this diet was only put out in 2003, so it was very new and didn't grab my attention at all. This diet, like the Ketogenic one, was designed more for people who can't be controlled on the medications alone, and I didn't see myself as falling into this category. I kept searching for a nutritional link and eventually came across a book called "Eat Right for Your Blood Type", written by Dr Peter J. D'Adamo and he states in his book that "...knowing your blood type is an important tool for understanding how your body reacts to food, your susceptibility to disease, your natural reaction to stress, and so much more."

I thought this was genius, so I bought the book immediately and started the diet. This diet specified all the foods for my blood type that made my system function at its best, as well as the foods that were going to act like poisons to me. I loved it, so I followed this nutrition model for a while and definitely started to feel better in my body and brain.

I was living with a good friend of mine Karen and trying to maintain my healthy lifestyle. I was meditating, well my version of it, and was into Bikram Yoga which, at that time, was just new on the trendy yoga scene and, strangely, the intense heat didn't seem to affect my brain chemistry. This was surprising, because heat was one of the things that had increased electrical activity for me in the past. I had been seeing a Kinesiologist for some time and found it to have great effects on aligning my body to my intuitive brain. Intuition, now there was a concept that I'd ignored and pushed away forever, so to start to connect with it finally was a weird and wonderful concept. I was so impressed with it and loved what it was doing for me. I decided this was going to be my new career path and I signed up to do a course in Advanced Kinesiology so I could start to assist in other people's healing. I was drug free, drinking a little bit but I referred to it as 'clean drinking'. I had made the connection that red wine (possibly due to the preservatives and the sugar would be my guess) and my brain farts were so clearly linked that I stopped drinking wine altogether. Every time I had wine, particularly red, I would wake up the next day with an overactive electrical brain which did, in rare cases, lead to a seizure. After documenting this for a while and experimenting with and without red wine, I could confidently say that the seizure activity diminished when I got off it.

Career wise, I was still floating around trying to find work with the least amount of responsibility in return for the maximum wage. With this belief system set firmly in place, I got a job working at a Rub and Tug (aka. an erotic massage parlour) as it was easy money and the hours suited me. Human behaviour, particularly male human behaviour fascinated me, but I didn't want to be a psychologist or counsellor, so instead I decided that pulling men off for money was a much better option into really understanding the human (male) mind. For those of you wondering what sort of logic and reasoning I came to at the time in order to get to this conclusion, I'm afraid I can't tell you because I really don't know. What I can tell you is that it was night work and due to the fact I was more of a morning seizure girl, this roster suited my brain much better as it decreased the potential to have a seizure before work. I worked there for six to eight months, both as an erotic masseuse and also in the laundry where there was no tugging allowed - just cleaning, lots of cleaning. I saw a lot in that time and heard a lot from the men. Most of the guys were really nice, and sure there was a physical element as to why they were there, but there were also a lot of men who needed another type of connection, the connection of being heard.

Just like a counsellor would be paid to listen, I too was paid to listen, but my counselling sessions would finish with a happy ending! I learnt that men all utilise the sex industry for different reasons. The white picket fence scenario is hard to maintain in a loveless relationship. The stress of financially keeping a large household together, intimacy being used as a commodity or a negotiating tool by their partners, single men, men who have suddenly lost their wives emotionally and/or sexually to child bearing and motherhood, death and so on. Towards the end of my time there it became clear to me that I had learned as much as I was going to learn and I needed to get out. My view of men had started to become a tad tainted, and I knew if I stuck around for much longer I would start to mistrust men, and I didn't want that to happen as I really wanted to find love, so Electro Girl yanked me out of there on the lightning bolt hovercraft and we beamed ourselves up and out of the building. She must have sensed it was time for me to have the happy ending instead! I quit in 2005 and very soon after that the universe sent me a version of love that was really going to teach me about being a bit more particular on my checklists when asking the universe to bring me love.

I was at Revolver, a nightclub in Melbourne, with some girlfriends and we were out on the town to have a good time and send off one of my best friends, Sarah, who was going off travelling overseas. I was chosen as the good time mascot and off I went to find us some party favours. I made my way around the half empty club asking a few people, trying to look like I knew what I was talking about, but was coming up stumps. I saw this guy on the dance floor busting out a few moves, so I sidled up next to him pretending I wanted to dance but really it was an intro to ask for the happy pills. I instantly became completely infatuated with his charisma, good looks and charm. We dated for three months and then I moved in with him (this was definitely a pattern I think).

G was a plumber when I met him, an ex-pastor, brought up in a Pentecostal world. He had just found his freedom from the church and was newly separated from his wife of 15 years. The healthy lifestyle and mindset I had created for myself and the dream of practising Kinesiology was about to be put on hold and replaced by partying hard, new friends, a marriage, a business, and a divorce all in the space of three years. This relationship brought up every fear and insecurity about love and trust I'd ever experienced and therefore Electro Girl was a big part of my time with G. She needed long service leave by the end of the relationship but she really was my knight in electric armour, forever there as a safety net when I went into seizure mode and needed to hide myself away on my own to see the seizure out.

We had a great, five bedroom, three bathroom house in the burbs, complete with an open fireplace and a cellar. The house had been designed around a contained open courtyard, and we had a huge garden out the back which was where we kept our four chooks and our suburban answer to a veggie garden. He had two awesome kids from his previous marriage who stayed with us whenever they could, we travelled around Australia and overseas, our lives were quite simplistic and we were comfortable.

We loved to entertain, and so together we would create these wild house parties. We built an underground club in the basement of our house which people still talk about to this day, nine years later, especially the massive NYE beach party we had one year. We hauled in a few trailer loads of sand and dumped it in the internal courtyard just to make it a real beach/dance floor. We both liked the element of doing something cool and exciting for people so they could really enjoy themselves and for this we were a great team. It took weeks to get the sand out of every crevice of the house but it was worth it.

The open courtyard looking like a beach

Over time, G and I decided to start a Grey Water business where he would set up the plumbing in people's houses to use the water from their laundries and disperse it onto their gardens. It was a relatively new and brilliant concept in the city at the time. We were both doing something that was good for the environment and that we could also live off. The charismatic man that I fell in love with was providing a stable home, a great friendship and bringing lots of fun to my life, but the scene in my head was slowly unravelling and becoming quite unstable due to a jealousy that I was finding hard to control.

You see, G loved the attention of women and, due to his conservative past and late birth into the scene of "sex, drugs, and rock n roll", it wasn't the sort of attention that ended up having any morals to it or that I could trust. I had always maintained that if he wanted to cheat on me that he should let me know first so I had the choice to stay or go before he got back home. In theory this was a great idea but in reality, someone who's just about to have an earth shattering shag fest isn't going to ring their partner to say, "Hey honey, I'm just about to shtoop this person senseless, I'll be home for dinner." I never got the phone call, so stayed locked inside my assumptions that he never had any extra-marital affairs.

I made allowances for all of this as it was truly a socially amazing time and it gave me the sense of having a home and a family which I wanted so badly even at the cost of my health. The scenario played out and had its crescendo at our wedding in March 2008. It was an outdoor wedding that we made into a weekend festival. Wedding on the Saturday, party Saturday night, and camp on the Sunday. The vision was large. We had our outfits made by a very talented costumier, Sarah Seahorse, who also designed my Electro Girl outfit on the cover. Our rings made by a jeweller who specialised in geometric patterns and I was carried down the aisle on a chariot by men in tight gold shorts and gold plated sunglasses.

We hired a few porta-loos, a massive generator, and catered for 120 of our nearest and dearest. We spent weeks at the site building

Me at my wedding being carried down the aisle by my groomsmen

and painting structures in order to create a venue for this wedding. We had DJs and a great sound system, laser lights, a teepee set up for a lounge area and 120 fitness balls flown in from China and blown up on site to be used as seats. The absolute piece de resistance was the 20 metre slip and slide we placed on an incline just next to the dance floor. We pumped up water from the nearby creek and fed it through a sprinkler with soap to better lubricate the slide. It was very very cool! The marriage ceremony was beautiful, the party was a success despite the guests sweltering in the 43 degree heat, and we were married.

Timna and Ray on the slip and slide at my wedding

Six weeks after the wedding something unforeseen happened and the following diary entry I wrote at the time will give you an indication of how something so wonderful turned to shit so quickly:

Diary Entry

2ND JULY 2008

I'm sitting at mum's because I've moved in for a brief time while I sort out this next stage of my life.

On the 7th of April, G and I decided to start a meditation course. It was an audio listening meditation that is designed to balance the two sides of your brain together, therefore balancing out your life. It was very calming and as we were trying to calm our party lives down a bit, we were hooked. They say from the moment you start the program, your brain starts changing and you should be able to see changes in your thinking and behaviour. Sounded great.

These changes are different for everyone and I felt no different. G didn't really either but he felt calmer. On April 20th, 10 days after we had started, G, myself, and four mates went to a bush dance. I really didn't want to go but I knew G would take drugs and I didn't feel comfortable leaving him to his own devices because sadly, I didn't trust him, so I went.

L.S.D was the drug of choice on this day and I refrained and chose to be the designated driver. Boy am I glad I did. When it was time to go and we all piled back in the van, G dug his heels in, freaked out and made me stop the van and basically stated that he was never going home again. He hated his life there and he was living a lie and he never wanted to be that man ever again. After six hours or so sitting in the cold listening to him regurgitate his hurtful "truths" which included the cheating on me that my gut feeling just knew, and that he never should have asked me to marry him, I eventually convinced him to come back home more so because I wanted to get out of the freezing cold. We were both exhausted by then and so off we went. Our friends had to call on a mate to come get them as we were so far from Melbourne that it would have been a two hour taxi ride or something.

This was the start of G's erratic behaviour. For three days he made out like he'd had an incredible spiritual awakening, but he was very emotional and not making heaps of sense. It passed briefly and he returned to the G I knew and loved. This was short lived though and four weeks later he really entered into Strangeville, which he wasn't budging from.

I'm in the marriage still, but I've had to take a step backwards for my own health and sanity due to G's behaviour at the moment. I honour that this is a process of healing but I'm not convinced that it's not from the drugs and, until he wants to admit it to himself and get an assessment to at least rule it out, I can't do much. My bad opinions of doctors and medicine have made me decide not to take him to a psychiatrist or get him put in an asylum and so I just have to try and ride out his head trip in the hope that he'll snap out of it.

In short, the fairy tale collided with reality with an unexpected bang. We bought a Volkswagen Transporter van, decked it out so it was liveable and went on a road trip to try and save the marriage and our future. We were due for a honeymoon anyway, so we stored all our stuff and took off to northern Queensland. I gave it six months before I was ready to admit to myself it was going nowhere for me. It was clearly now all about him and his "awakening", and there was no room for us in the story to grow together except if I wanted to be his anchor and follow his path. He wanted to spread his wings, live the "spiritual" life, look deep inside himself and fuck every woman that crossed his path. The dream was over and it was heartbreaking for me, but I had to cut him loose. Suddenly I was faced with my own divorce! Divorce, my nemesis! The concept that started my electrically unstable existence at 14 was now in my face again, but I was now the creator of it for myself.

After three years of living in yet another emotionally unstable environment, adding to that copious amounts of drugs and alcohol and now on top of that coping with the worst heartache I had experienced to date, it was time to get back on track and the plan was:

a) Brace myself

b) Get a place to live

c) Return to the healthy living template that I put on hold

d) Surround myself with supportive people

e) Find a caring GP to work with to find a solution to the seizures

f) Remain positive and stay focused on the end result which was once again in the forefront of the picture - how to live without seizures as naturally as possible

Some people say I have attitude - maybe I do...
but I think you have to. You have to believe in yourself
when no one else does - that makes you a winner right there.

Venus Williams

CHAPTER 8

You Can't Do That!

As you are now aware, my diagnosis of epilepsy was established at 19. "Big deal, it's just a diagnosis, it doesn't define you," was what I was hearing from loved ones. The world was my oyster, I could do whatever I wanted to do, my whole life was ahead of me and all I had to do was choose a direction.

Great, I want to be a pilot... "Umm, sorry, but that's not allowed if you have epilepsy, as you need to be perfect and you're a tad flawed."

Alright then, I want to go scuba diving on the Great Barrier Reef... "Yeah about that; apologies, but not that either. Your brain is too delicate and unpredictable and you may implode under the water."

Ok, well I want to skydive, OMG that looks like so much fun come on, come on. "Nope, that one is off the list too, a seizure at 8000 feet isn't covered by our insurance."

Well I'm totally going to donate my brain and organs to research when I die. "Hate to tell you this, but they don't want your organs, they'll be trashed by all the drugs you've had to take and your brain is too delicate for research. Why don't you play the tambourine... that's fun!"

I never wanted to hear the words "No you can't", which is why I hid my symptoms from family, friends and strangers for as long as possible. I didn't want to believe there was anything wrong with me, and if I told people I had epilepsy, I thought they would treat me differently. If I didn't tell anyone, I'd be able to do all the things I wanted to do and not have to feel like I needed to be wrapped in cotton wool. The decision became an easy one. I just wouldn't tell new people I met if I felt they didn't need to know. The type of seizures I experience would never just happen randomly. I would always get warnings in the form of head hiccups, and 90% of them happened in the mornings before anyone ever saw me, so I felt like I knew myself well enough to back up this decision. I never once stopped to think about the safety and wellbeing of others, as my lack of disclosure was more about protecting me from a label I didn't want to be associated with more than about worrying how seeing me have a seizure might affect them.

In 2010 I met a few girls in Mullumbimby, a small town I was living in at the time in Northern NSW. They mentioned a Roller Derby team was about to start initiating members and the try outs were in a few days. At the time I had no idea what Roller Derby was except that it was an all girls contact sport on roller skates. I went for try outs, fell in love with being back on roller skates after nearly 25 years, and my alter ego, Roller Derby persona 'Paris EataMole' was born!

Paris EataMole

There were a few girls on the team who knew I had epilepsy but I didn't think it was one of those things I needed to let the rest of the team know at the beginning stages. I desperately wanted to immerse myself in this and I didn't want to hear "NO", so I made an executive decision to hold off on telling anyone until I knew I was going to be skating on a regular basis.

Roller Derby became not only a sport I played for fun, competition, and fitness, but the girls I skated with became a second family. The sport granted me courage, strength, friendship, an understanding of teamwork, and a trust in my abilities like nothing else I've ever done. More than that, I was free of my condition whilst I was on skates. I never once thought about the possibility of having a seizure whilst on track which was liberating as every other second of the day there was an underlying fear which was palpable for me, but the circuitry in my brain never once jack-knifed in the four years that I skated.

Four months into skating, I decided to come clean about my condition and explain the minimal possibility for seizures, to the president of the league. I approached her, told her my story, and explained how embarrassed I felt about the seizures and being labelled and how I didn't think I needed to mention it earlier because I didn't know how long I'd be skating for initially. She wasn't impressed that I hadn't said anything previously, but she still liked me at that stage, so I was reprimanded with a rap on the knuckles and my confession was accepted.

Months later she and I had an altercation about something completely unrelated, which then set her on a personal mission to burn me at the stake and use her powers as the president of the league to expel me. The non-disclosure of my seizures was a perfect weapon to assist her in this vendetta and make an example out of me to the rest of the team. All of a sudden she was furious that I had put her and the rest of the team in danger and broke the league's terms and conditions by not initially disclosing my medical history, which could of potentially hurt someone else if I'd had a seizure on track. It was put to a vote by the team and I was ordered to pack up my skates and piss off. I was heartbroken and devastated that my "family" could just turn on me like that, but I had to suck it up. All my issues about abandonment came rushing forth and so episodes of seizure activity came riding to my aid on a white horse to save me from what little inner peace I was trying to hold on to.

Ten months later, the President left the league and I was asked to return and play with the most awesome team of girls. I played successfully with them for three years and never once was my condition an issue. They just accepted it as part of me and were ready to assist if I needed it. In fact, I joined another team when I moved to Melbourne in 2014 and ran straight to their first aid crew to inform them about my condition and their response was, "OK, thanks, as long as you let us know what we need to do, you don't have to tell anyone else unless you want to, it's your business!" Seems like a much more compassionate and supportive approach to me.

The question myself, and possibly many other seizure inflicted people ponder is; when is the right time to tell people and which people do you tell? Many people have told me along the way that epilepsy is just a small part of who I am and that is true if you are on the right treatment to control the seizures, be it holistic, alternative, or prescribed. When you aren't on the right prevention treatment and are experimenting, you become a bit of a loaded gun and it does become a huge part of who you are and what you do. Do you disclose this at a job interview and risk being judged, discriminated against, and considered a weak link because you have epilepsy? Sure, there is equal opportunity employment out there but you will still be seen as a person with a medical problem and the issues you experience from the side effects of medication may come into play, even if you aren't having seizures. Many anti-epileptic drugs make you drowsy, give you double vision, affect your mood and make it impossible to multitask due to concentration issues plus many more, so whilst you may think you're doing a fabulous job, your boss and colleagues may think you're not handling the tasks well and perhaps are not suited for the position.

What about a first date, a one night stand or new friends you meet? Is it necessary to disclose this information straight up, so you know who you're dealing with and if it will be a problem for them if they see you have a seizure? This may sound dramatic and a bit far-fetched, but it is a very real scenario in which a person can be so freaked out by seeing a seizure that they buckle under the pressure. This happened to me with a good friend of mine, who saw me have a seizure in her living room whilst I was living with her and didn't get over it for months. It wasn't long after the seizure that I had to look for other accommodation because she wasn't comfortable with her own ability to deal with possibly seeing me have another one at that stage. It really shook her foundations and it took her months to recover. It can be a very scary experience for the onlooker, especially those who have never seen one before. Thankfully she didn't call an ambulance as they cost a fortune and 90% of the time, depending on the type of seizure, don't even need to be called. The more people become aware of how to deal with them, the less fear, panic and stigma will be associated with them. A lot of assisting someone with a seizure is being resilient and realising it's just a circuitry issue.

The seizure will see itself out, you just have to remain calm, stick around as a watcher, remove anything from the immediate area that could cause harm to the person, and smile once they come out of it because you will be their first reality check back into the conscious world. If you're looking freaked out, it's going to make it so much worse for the person having the seizure.

Another example of how non-disclosure can go pear shaped was when I was house sitting for a friend and her brother in law needed to stay over for a night. That particular evening I got to bed around midnight and woke up three hours later to pee out the litres of booze I had consumed only hours earlier. I remember walking back from the toilet, the head hiccups started, and boom, my anxiety immediately kicked in about him seeing me have a seizure. He had told me that he'd never seen a seizure before when we'd discussed it briefly earlier that night, and I had told him a little about what it involved, but nothing really prepares you for seeing one as your response is something no-one can prepare you for. He was fast asleep and I thought I'd be able to get through it without him even knowing. I was petrified, anxious and losing my ability and strength to fight this seizure off with calming thoughts. The last thing I remember was lying in bed naked feeling very vulnerable and mentally repeating the words "Please, please, please no, not now."

When I came back to consciousness, there were two ambulance drivers looking at me and asking if I knew my name, where I was, and if I was ready to go to the hospital. The hospital was only 100 metres down the road, so they didn't even get time to turn their sirens on after they'd loaded me in the ambulance. I repeatedly told them I was ok and they could leave, as I just needed to sleep but apparently they had a legal obligation to take me to the hospital because they'd been called by the brother in law. He did what he thought was best and made his decision based on his fear and my lack of explanation to him. The blood on the carpet from the carpet burn created by my face rubbing against it was what sparked him to call them as well as it looked like a bit of a crime scene so I don't blame the poor guy. That 100 metre ambulance ride came with an invoice of $300.

The letter I wrote to get out of the ambulance payment:

21st December 2009
Attn. Finance Manager,

In the month of October, I was house sitting at a friend's place in Mullumbimby, NSW, whilst they were overseas for five weeks. There was another person house sitting as well. I have been dealing with epilepsy for 16 or more years now. I had informed this person of this as a "just in case" thing and told him not to ring the ambulance if I ended up having a seizure and just to place me in a comfortable position and remove harm from my way and let me just get through it.

Well, on the night of 21/10/09, I started to 'jolt', as I call it and I usually take a Valium and it passes. I didn't do this, as I thought I'd go back to sleep.

I went into a seizure state, and he found me convulsing, naked, on the floor, and basically freaked out. I was on carpet, so through the convulsions, my nose was rubbing on the carpet, hence the blood on my nose, and he had no idea what to do, so he rang the ambulance.

After I came back into consciousness and was already walking around, I realised what was happening and saw the ambulance staff waiting for me to get ready, and I questioned why they were there. I told them I didn't want to go and it was a standard thing but they made me. I only went with them because I thought they wouldn't possibly charge me for a 100 metre ride.

I should also point out at this stage that the hospital is two doors down from the house I was in and I walked home perfectly fine three hours after.

I don't believe that I need to pay for his fear, and I told the ambulance drivers that I didn't want to go. I feel I did everything to avoid this $300 fee, and therefore I have no intention of paying it!

Yours Sincerely,
Lainie Chait

I have tried to avoid having the seizures in front of people at all costs because the negative public experiences kept bringing the concept home that having public seizures is a thing to be embarrassed about. To think people are scared of seeing a part of me that I have to deal with so often, but which I have no control over, really saddens me, especially as I have no idea what I look like in the throes of a seizure. Thus, I have to live it through the eyes of the spectator. The more freaked out they look, the more I want to keep hiding myself away so I made sure I always had an exit strategy wherever I went in order to have somewhere to escape so I could have the seizures on my own. After years of studying myself and how and when they would come, predicting them and escaping became much easier for me. Myself and possibly many other seizure inflicted people just want to protect YOU from seeing US but in doing this, as I've learnt the hard way, hiding away is only going to stop people from having an awareness about what to do and how to assist.

Over the years I've learnt that who, how, and when you tell people gets easier the more you detach yourself from making it the centre of your life. I did actually go skydiving in 2008 from 11,000 feet but I didn't disclose my medical predicament. Judge me if you will, but I was getting to know myself intimately by this stage and was in close tune with my wiring issues and because of this, it was easier to have faith that nothing would occur. I didn't work myself into a frenzy about it, which potentially would have raised my threshold to having a seizure. I just embarked on it and did a tandem jump over Mission Beach in Queensland Australia. It was gorgeous, it was on my bucket list and, as I suspected, nothing happened. As it turned out, my ex hubby should have re-thought his jump more than me, as he suffered motion sickness and came down vomiting in a bag from 9000 feet. This was our last adventure together and from where I sat watching him come down hurling – possibly the best!

If we cannot execute a level of mind greater than how we emotionally feel, we will never relate to anything unknown or unpredictable.

Joe Dispenza

CHAPTER 9

Revelations

Over the years, the large task of trying to heal myself of epilepsy through various modalities was never ending and had the same feeling as being caught in a Groundhog Day. I have had over 250 Grand Mal seizures over 25 years. Of those, around 200 of them I chose to have on my own, away from the eyes of people that could potentially reject me if they saw one. As scary as they were, I got used to them and I didn't have to deal with the embarrassment and shame if I was on my own, only the internal failure monologues of having had another one.

I've explained so far what the triggers were and the symptoms related to them, but now I will illustrate the personal seizure scenario I used to engage with in my body and mind.

I would feel a seizure coming on, head hiccups, misfiring, temperature rising. *Is it going to happen - shit!* The head hiccups could last anywhere between five to ten minutes if there was no anxiety, and 30 minutes if I was really struggling to contain them. Then the anxiety would kick in and I would start to feel claustrophobic, like there was no escape from this entity that was going to take over me. I would try to prevent it through breathing or positive thinking or masturbating or watching cartoons or anything really; anything that would take my mind away from the impending embarrassment and feelings of failure. If none of that worked, I'd try to make it to the toilet to have a panic poo. This was always a sign to me I was going to have a Grand Mal and to brace myself. From having to take a panic poo to knowing I'd be having a Grand Mal would be about five to ten minutes. I still think it was an odd warning signal but, without fail, every time I had a seizure, I would need to take a dump first. I feel quite lucky that I had the urge to go before as many seizure afflicted people can lose control of their bladders/bowels during the seizure.

If there was someone with me watching this internal and external struggle I went through, I would reassure them and myself that "It will all be ok, nothing will happen, it will pass, nothing to worry about", and to my credit, I really believed it would. When the anxiety got too much and took over, I did end up in a state of acceptance that it was going to happen and if I was on my own, I would put myself in a safe position with enough time to brace myself and then boom, I'd wake up after the show to pick up the pieces. As soon as I became aware after coming back into consciousness from a seizure, I would clean up the pool of saliva next to me (this has always been what I look for when I'm on my own as a sign that I've had a seizure), get dressed, crack a joke to the person shaking in the corner who'd just witnessed it all, and I was out the door like nothing had happened, in an attempt to prove to myself there was nothing wrong with me.

The gentler approach would have been to acknowledge that my mind and body had just been through a tremendous amount of stress and trauma, and what I really needed was to rest for as long as my mind and body needed. I'm not really that important that the world can't live without me for half a day, or even a full day, it was just in my head that I needed to get up and be functional.

I remember one experience from 2011, where I was living in an awesome self-contained caravan out the back of a friend's house. The toilet was outside, down a few steps and about 20 metres away from the caravan.

In this instance I woke up around eight o'clock in the morning and within five minutes the misfiring started and I was fighting my brain, getting scared, trying to be tough, trying to call in all my relaxing mantras, Electro Girl, sound recordings of whale farts, anything to stop this force from bearing down on me. In doing all of this, I just kept falling over and when I tried to get up, I would drop to the ground again. When I needed to do that pre-seizure panic poo, I had no choice, I had to get up and at least try to make a bee line for the toilet. In this instance, I knew I couldn't make it to the toilet even 20 metres away because I kept falling over, so I looked around for another option, great, an empty bucket by the door. I was in fight or flight mode so I had no choice but to poo in a bucket in the caravan, hoping I could then just chill out and ride the rest of the seizure out safely.

With that out of the way, I lay down to put myself in a safe place, so I could finally pass out, but I couldn't relax because the bucket of shit was right there right in my face. It was a caravan, so everything is right there in your face, that's the beauty of small space living. I should have just not concerned myself with it, but unfortunately the niggling anxiety of someone coming in and seeing my shit in the bucket whilst I was unconscious was devastating to me at the time. So in the nude, my bucket o' poo and I made our way to the toilet. This innocent 20 metre trip to the loo was a grand mistake because, just as I stepped outside the caravan, my brain misfired so strongly that my whole system went into shock and I went down hard, the bucket went flying, and poo was flung all over the path. That's the last thing I remember.

From the story I was told by my beautiful house mate, Mirra, who came out to look after me, the story unfolded like this. While I was having a seizure on the path, literally in my own faeces and my shitty bucket was lying next to me, the inflatable pool our friend/landlady had bought for our summer entertainment was being filled up for us to use over the weekend. Ironically, she had forgotten about it and at the same time as I was lying on the path, the pool had overfilled and was gushing over the side wildly onto me. Luckily Mirra is one cool, calm and collected individual as she handled all of this without so much of a bat of an eyelid and kept me safe. At least the overflowing pool washed the evidence of the contents of the bucket away!

I have always had this weird ego related to having epilepsy. I saw myself as this invincible type of character, different from everyone else and much stronger than the average person because I deal with this shit day to day and survive it. Ego might sound like a strange word to use, but in my case, Ego has played a huge role in the story. Ego wasn't going to accept I was different and 'ill'. Ego stopped me from connecting with people. Ego became a turning point revelation. Much later on, once the gloves had come off, the punching bag that I had been using as a metaphor for my emotional wellbeing was begging for mercy. If things were going to change for me, I needed to admit to myself that I was a seizure snob, a heroic victim if you will. I never wanted to associate with the condition and, therefore, even talking with other people with epilepsy was not of importance to me, as it meant I was making that association for myself.

There was an element about having epilepsy that allowed me to wear the underachiever hat, the apathetic hat, the hat that allowed me to give up really easy and quickly on things and not get judged by the world for it due to having an "excuse". This hat also allowed me to hide my heart from lovers and partners. Herein lies yet another irony because I wanted people to see me as someone who could do anything, but I was more focused on those accolades socially, more than professionally and therefore have never really pushed myself to achieve in the business world. I have never had a problem getting the jobs I wanted and, luckily for me, I have never experienced any discrimination due to the affliction.

The recurring theme for the last 20 years has been "What is it about having seizures I just can't seem to accept?" and "Why have I let it take over my world and cause so much embarrassment and shame within?"

The more I am forced to look at these questions, the more I have to ensure a gentleness with myself, so I don't condemn myself for the way I chose to deal with it.

What I'm finding more and more apparent now that I am letting people know about epilepsy is that many people still really don't have a connection to what it is. The majority of people have either seen a seizure randomly, had a friend at school who had them, a colleague at work or they have never seen one at all. I myself, have only ever personally met four people who have epilepsy (that I know of) and yet, as stated on the Epilepsy Action Australia website, "an estimated 50 million people around the world have epilepsy at any given time"(2). How come more people haven't seen a seizure and know what to do? Why does it still frighten the onlookers and isolate the people who have seizures? I still suffer from embarrassment at asking for help if I'm in a place where I know no-one (thankfully this doesn't happen often). If I'm around friends and family, I feel much safer now and, to be honest, quite relieved to have the help, knowing I'll come out on the flip side with my face intact and all my bits where they should be.

Diary Entry:

28TH SEPTEMBER 2011

Who am I kidding!!! I really need to see someone about this. I'm feeling really helpless and very alone, even though I have so many people around me. I can't seem to work it out. To me it all seems so fucking hard. I'm a victim of my own epileptic creation and I'm lonely. I just want someone to help me through this. I just want to lead a normal existence where I'm not thinking every waking moment of epilepsy.

So it's becoming more and more evident that my ego is driving me, so much so that it wants my spirit to not be free, because then it will die and egos don't like to die!

I've got so much sadness that is sitting in my cells just waiting to be let out in the form of deep crying. Not even words, just tears. Repressed anger, sitting there not wanting to be spoken just yelled out to the ether. All the while my soul, spirit, driving force, light is waiting patiently underneath for an answer and I think finally it's going to get a chance to shine.

If I admit I have epilepsy then I'm admitting I have a medical problem, and I'm still so fucking sure that it's emotional that I feel like I'd be lying to myself.

That has been the conundrum for my whole existence with this.

I have seizures, but I'm not an epileptic. That's what I'm prepared to admit and work with, because that feels honest. I have seizures and electrical misfires because I repress a lot and for some reason have carried a pattern of being unworthy. Bringing it all to the surface means that there will be nothing left underneath that I need to escape.

Leave fear behind and take chances in life.

Start to breathe properly and talk to a counsellor.

I Love Me.

My ego no longer needs to control me. No more hiding behind normality.

Truth and Living in the present

As my ego starts melting, I am turning my focus out more than in and I have become quite humbled by the realisation that my struggle is no different to anyone else's on this earth. That this journey I have been so embedded in, where I thought I was so different to everyone else is really just me playing my part in evolving for the greater good of the planet. My part just so happened to have seizures in the plot. As my ego starts melting and I take responsibility for my actions, I see how I can use this story as a tool for connection to others struggling with their own individual conditions, instead of disconnection. As my ego starts melting I am now feeling love where a vortex of fear, loathing and lack of self-worth used to live.

You cannot change your future, but,
you can change your habits
and surely your habits will
change your future.

Dr Abdul Halam

CHAPTER 10

The Scientific Proof

Thankfully, in 2009 I met a man called Torsten through Ray and Eliza. A very smart individual who, amongst many other interests, has a very broad range of knowledge about all things scientific... especially the workings of the brain. He helps people by researching information on their behalf, which sets them on a path of exploration about their own affliction, in order for them to work towards fixing themselves.

Torsten, like Ray and Eliza, encourages individuals to learn more about the plants that provide us with food and medicine, so the knowledge about them is kept alive and utilised. He brings a scientific approach to herbs and plants that highlights their biology, chemistry and pharmacology. He juggles from one potential answer to another and encouraging me to do the same and has always been available for me to pick his brains if I need to (no pun intended).

Torsten made me want to learn more about how my brain actually functioned and when I got stressed or emotional, why my brain would fire off uncontrollable sparks that would end up in these jerking actions to the outside world. When I finally woke up to the fact the work had to be done internally as well as externally with the aid of practitioners, I paid more attention to the science side of the brain and healing. The herbs and alternative healing therapies were taking up one side of the coin in the experience, but through meeting other people who get off on neurological science, this whole new world was opening up for me around just how our brains work and how we have more control than we think in reprogramming our minds. There is a significant amount of information available to people through the web about the science of the brain that is written in layman's terms and is easily digestible, even for people with a low attention span like me. NLP (Neurolinguistic Programming), EFT (Emotional Freedom Technique), neuroplasticity, and even mindfulness stress based meditation all work on reprogramming old limiting beliefs and thought patterns with worldwide success.

Once your health reaches a place where you need medical assistance, then management becomes about handing over the reins of your life to a specialist as they're the ones who have spent years studying and are supposed to have the knowledge in the field relevant to your situation. This is what the majority of us do as no one wants to be sick and the majority of humans are all innately afraid of death, so a popular option is to take the magic pill prescribed by a specialist in order to get better as quickly as possible. People don't really dance with the fact that they are an integral part in creating their own management plan. It's almost like, when we fall sick, our self-worth and self-confidence fall sick as well and we no longer have faith that we can help ourselves, so we put all our faith and power in someone else to heal us. From where I sit now, passing the proverbial torch, this is a dangerous move!

I came to the conclusion after being off the meds for nine years that it might be time to look into a better management plan for myself as my brain still wasn't functioning at its optimum. I went to see the local doctor in the town I was living and ended up starting on a complete health journey with his wife, Ann-Mary, which to this day has changed my life. Ann-Mary is a registered nurse, qualified naturopath and has spent the last 20 years applying holistic therapies and running successful natural medical centres specialising in nutritional and environmental medicine. We worked very closely together, and she was everything I was looking for in a practitioner. She had the knowledge and experience to assist me but didn't claim to know what was best for me, and I really respected her for that.

She educated me on the health of my gut and diet in relation to my nervous system, and we dove straight in to getting my levels of zinc, magnesium, and B vitamins in check. Did you know that many people with seizure and anxiety disorders have some degree of deficiency or biologically unavailable zinc, magnesium and Vitamin B6? My levels were very low when I started working with her and these are essential for the nervous system to function properly. I'm happy to say that she restored my faith in practitioners who care and really set me on a path to want to get a good management plan happening for myself so I can lead the extraordinary life I came here to live, instead of a life of fear and ill health.

Gut health has since become an extremely talked about topic in regards to the "gut-brain connection". One man who stands out to me in his research of this is a neurologist by the name of Dr David Perlmutter. His research applies to epilepsy, ADHD, early onset dementia, Parkinson's, MS and depression.

In his studies he talks about inflammation in the gut and an unhealthy microbiome being the number one nemesis of healthy neurological function and optimum brain health. Having a healthy gut microbiome actually reduces and controls inflammation. Although gut microbiome gets compromised through the taking of things like antibiotics, sugar, gluten, drinking fluoride in our water system, eating processed foods and more. He has written a few books based on his research but his recent book 'Brain Maker' which has become an international best seller, really brought home to me that what is happening in my intestines, has a direct effect on the functioning of my brain and I've been on a journey to address this ever since.

No man is worth his salt who is not ready at all times
to risk his well-being, to risk his body,
to risk his life in a great cause.

Theodore Roosevelt

CHAPTER 11

Leaving the Comfort Zone

I stayed single for six years after the break up with my ex-husband. I had officially become "off limits." I basically had a "do not enter" sign around my neck, and that was the way it was going to be. I tried a few one night stands, thinking, "Come on Lain, you've got to get back on the horse, there's a lot of horses out there that need riding." One particular memory goes a little something like this:

Girl meets guy, girl gets drunk, guy comes back to girl's house, guy and girl get jiggy with it, girl has seizure, convulses and passes out, guy runs away so quickly after girl came back to consciousness from a morning seizure that he left a trail of his clothes down her driveway. You know, just the usual one night stand scenario.

Myself and my house mate at the time were so amused by his trail of desperation to get out of our house we left one of his socks in our driveway for a few months as a kind of memorial flag to his 'great escape'. After I was confronted by the idea that the surrounding Op shops couldn't fit any more clothes in their 'male' sections from me, I came to the conclusion, for my sanity and emotional safety, that the easiest thing to do was just give up the idea of intimacy altogether. At the time, this was a much better option than not appearing strong, sexy, and in control.

It was at this stage that a negative shift happened within me and I started to feel a lot more "fear" around the seizures. For the first time, I started to actually think about the seizures as something happening to me in the present, rather than fixating on it as something that had just happened and that I needed to prevent and cure. As the focus turned to the now, so did the fear and anxiety of future seizures and I was slowly starting to become a bit more of a victim (although I would never have admitted it or been conscious of it at that stage in time). Fear was overriding me and casting a massive shadow where light used to be. It was starting to consume me mentally, emotionally, and psychologically, but my positive approach to life and humour kept me optimistic and afloat. Optimism was always accessible to me, and good humour and wit were my saviours.

This shadow which was looming over me had never been there before but I'd say, because of the decades of daily fear of being caught out, having misfires, electrical episodes and even seizures, it was all starting to catch up with me. The constant self-shame and embarrassment I felt daily was getting too much for even the greatest optimist to deal with. The two things consistently making me smile at the time were a weekly community radio show I presented called 'The Booty Call', and Roller Derby, where I skated like Olivia Newton John in Xanadu but way more aggressive and much less gracefully. The radio show covered topics on sexuality and was quite risqué which, thankfully, the audience and the community radio station Bay FM welcomed. I covered topics from circumcision to prostitution to sexual fetishes and everything in between. Part of why I liked it was I was hidden in a studio, so if I did have a twitch or a misfire, no one could see me and because I could always switch to playing songs, go get some air, breathe deeply, or reach for a Valium. It was all about whatever worked at the time.

There was only one night in the six years of broadcasting that I was close to having a seizure on air. I was trying to do the show and ignore the signs, thinking "I'm hidden, it will all be cool." But the electrical misfires just wouldn't stop and I didn't want to stop either, as I was enjoying myself. It then started to go from head hiccups to the very distinct signs that I was going to hit the deck. I ended the show early, called Oly, the afterhours security guy who happened to be a good friend of mine, and by the time he came, I was in the midst of a seizure on the floor. I hadn't prepared him, and he had no idea what to do, but he was there when I came back to consciousness. I had a little less skin on my face from the carpet burn and he looked quite freaked out, but I was safe, we both survived it and my radio fans were none the wiser.

In 2013, I decided I needed to spread my wings a bit and have an adventure, so I booked a trip overseas. I spent some of my time at a Roller Derby convention in Las Vegas with 5,000 other derby freaks, and did a little travelling around Mexico and other parts of the USA for a total of eight weeks. The thought of travelling away from my comfort zone of Byron Bay was exciting, necessary, and so mother fucking scary that I had to really ignore the fear and stick with the program, despite my dread of possibly losing my shit in a faraway place with only a medical dog tag around my neck as a buffer zone. A few weeks before I left, I got a mild concussion from having a Grand Mal. It scared the shit out of me but, in saying that, it also knocked some sense in to me and I came to realise that if I continued on the path of fearing leaving my comfort zone, I would always be a prisoner to the seizures and it would rule the way I lived my life forever.

Diary Entry:
22ND MAY 2013

Finally got concussion from a seizure. I remember the hour before trying desperately to talk myself out of it, getting anxious, popping Valium, needing to take the obligatory dump, the feeling of claustrophobia, bracing myself, and then waking up on the ground. I was on my own again, which I'm thankful for as this one was messy. It was freaky and traumatic and I hated every minute of the lead up to the seizure and the week to follow, but something feels different about this one. The whole week I felt like an understudy in the screenplay of my life. I was experiencing things and going places and doing things, but I wasn't present at all, and felt things from a distance even if the person I was talking to was right in front of me. To the medical world, it was called concussion. To me, well yeah, it was called concussion, but it was a wake up call as well.

I cried a lot and released a lot of emotion during that week. A friend sat with me for six hours in emergency whilst I waited for a CAT scan to see if I'd fucked my brain from the hit (which I hadn't) and honestly, something has shifted in me about this. I am going to start taking control of the way I deal with it because the way that I'm going about it now is not empowered, not healing, and not nurturing. It's fearful and lonely and I don't need to do it that way anymore. No need to hide it. Deal with the fear and keep reminding myself how amazing I am to be dealing with this on a daily basis with optimism about finding a way of managing this condition and still grabbing life by the balls and having fun!

Part of my overseas adventure was to go to a massive six day festival in the United States called 'Burning Man'. After tossing up the pros and cons of whether this was a good idea for me and really struggling with my 'fear of missing out' personality, which hovered over me like a vulture looking for fresh meat trying to convince me to go, I decided to sell my ticket. Challenging myself by travelling on my own was one thing, but exposing myself to an environment that was going to be very tempting on all levels, partying in the boiling Nevada desert, was going to be too exhausting for both myself and Electro Girl. I humbly told the vulture to piss off, and planned other fabulous things to do instead that didn't involve faux fur outfits and public displays of nudity.

After the ticket was sold and a brief outline of where I was going to go was put on paper, my trip was planned. Everything I owned was placed in a storage cabinet in Byron Bay, work responsibilities were passed on, medicine was purchased, bags were packed, medical alert necklace was on, and all I needed to do was get on a plane and head to Vegas, baby - for RollerCon. The thought of six days eating, sleeping, shitting and partying on roller skates was orgasmically exciting. The whole time there, I was very mindful of not pushing the party boundaries too far, and so I indulged in social pleasantries but made sure I had the balance of enough rest when I needed to. I was staying in a room with two girls from my team and they knew of my seizure disorder so I felt safe to just wing it, live without fear of having a seizure, and simply play my cards and see what happened. As it turns out, I was fine, no mishaps and no worries. Met lots of people, had a few shags, engaged in the nightlife, drank and roller skated excessively. The only thing I didn't do there was get married by an Elvis impersonator, but I figure that's probably a good thing.

From Vegas I went directly to Mexico for four weeks. This was the part of the trip I was longing for and also secretly dreading as I had left the safety of travelling in a group and was suddenly on my own and challenging myself to be fearless. I didn't really ease my way into Mexico. I basically started my travels on a little party island called Isla Mujeres and checked into a bed and breakfast which was a bit of a three star dive and not oozing with comfort, but to me it was a sanctuary, just in case my switch tripped and I needed an escape plan. It took me half a day to get my bearings, and then the island became a paradise. Met people that day, partied with them at night and spent the rest of the week travelling around, sightseeing, dancing, drinking, swimming, laughing and sunbathing. No episodes of anything electrically unstable happened, and my confidence was building that I may even escape this whole trip without one seizure. Praise the lord!

I left the island after a week and spent three weeks travelling to Tulum, San Cristobal, Oaxaca and Bacalar. I swam in stalactite caves, snorkelled with turtles, hiked through old ruins, met loads of people, ate amazing food, drank way too much Mescal and fell in love with feeling free from my mind's shackles. Truth be told, I was never fully "free" from the shackles as I was always worried about having a seizure. I could never really keep the "what ifs" from my mind, but I'd met an awesome German girl early in my travels and we got along really well and she wanted to be around me and travel where I did through Mexico, so we sort of teamed up together. Thanks to her I felt my back was being watched; another angel in my story, I believe.

Diary Entry from Overseas:

14TH SEPTEMBER 2013

Six weeks into the experience and I have had a wonderful time. I have had two Grand Mal seizures in that time but, as usual, they were wonderfully, undeniably self-inflicted. The first one only happened a month into the trip so even though I was drinking every night pretty much, I was looking after myself with sleep and food and was fuelled up with total excitement about being away, so the adrenaline was wonderful. The first seizure was in Caye Caulker (an island in Mexico). Way too much alcohol, late night and had some men interested in me which always sends me into a fluster :-). The second one was in San Cristobal caused by way too much alcohol, hardly any sleep and, as I found out later, my period came two days later. Both seizures were in the morning, in bed, and I was surprisingly really cool and calm about it. I did attempt Valium on both occasions but these attempts to curb the excitement in my brain fell by the wayside.

There was a girl I met in Caye Caulker. We were both staying in the same hostel room and we hit it off immediately. I told her within the first hour or so of meeting her that I had epilepsy and showed her my dog tag so she could read what to do. I must say, the dog tag was a brilliant idea as I don't have to tell people now, they can read and ask the questions they want to know. It has the medi alert symbol and reads like this:

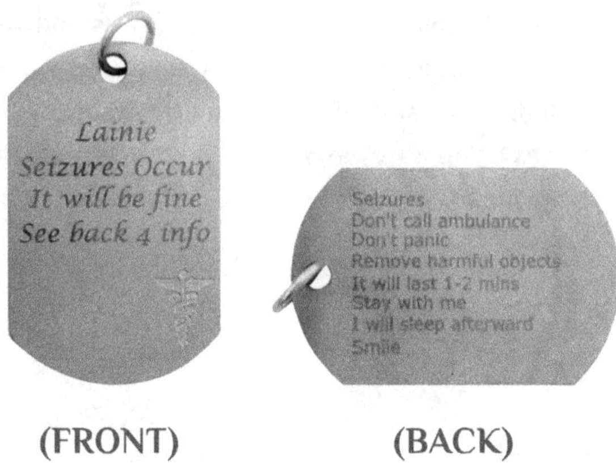

(FRONT) (BACK)

I didn't think to write it in Spanish so it was lucky I was around many other English speaking travellers. Anyway, I digress, I felt really comfortable around Sasha and knew instantly that I would be fine if I had a seizure around her. Well, the first seizure was in our hostel room. I woke up, looked over at her sleeping, knew it was going to be a mission to wake her as we were out drinking until the wee hours, but I was totally relaxed to have a seizure. I didn't stress out and build a huge anxious trip around it and just left it to the universe that if she was going to wake up during it, that she'd be cool. She didn't wake up, I had the seizure and the day went on as usual.

The second seizure was the same type of scenario, hostel room in the morning, another girl asleep, Sasha at brekky, reach for the Valium, have to take the standard ablution about 15 mins before, then boom... thanks for coming, see you in half hour.

Sasha came into the room during it, the other girl was quite calm about it all.

That trip away did change things in my head for me. I stood and looked fear in the face and said "Fear, one of us is going to lose this battle in a big way so you either go hassle the billions of other people that want to live in fear or you work with me here, but you are not ruling the roost, buddy, it's show time."

The diary entry was written as I was leaving Mexico. I met up with friends after Mexico and travelled to San Francisco where I just lapped up everything visually. My heart was open again and I had a glimpse back into what it was like to not live every moment in fear of having a seizure. I remember being taken to my first gay night club. My friend Eliza and I were really the only girls in this club and there was a lot of hair from what I remember. These were bears we were hanging out with - the hairy bears. I felt like we'd been let into a secret society and I was just a starry eyed middle aged woman trying to blend in with 400 half-naked, hairy gay men. As a woman in my 40's, I'm starting to get facial hair anyway, so in a roundabout way I sort of felt like I was amongst my own.

There were some things I witnessed in that bar that would fall into the category of "What happens in San Fran, stays in San Fran," but I will say, I saw my very first dance floor blow job. Something I would never have experienced if I had been living in fear on my couch in Byron Bay. The facial hair yes, but the gay bar no, and all of SF's wondrous beauty that came along with the bar as well.

Whilst I was in the USA, particularly in the California leg of my visit, my intention was to find some doctors to have a chat about the wildly political topic of medicinal marijuana for epilepsy. Medicinal marijuana is a legal medicine in 25 States of the USA at present, for those who can convince their doctor that they need it for their medical conditions. It is still illegal to possess and sell for recreational purposes, but for medicinal reasons, the tide seems to have turned. I thought it would be an easy task to source out and chat with doctors who provide the medical cards to people as well as the growers who are well educated in which strains of the plant are used for cases like mine. My mindset was to chat with them, pick their brains a bit, maybe take some seeds back to Australia and start to grow my own and medicate myself with the correct procedure handed down from some experts and professionals, all illegally of course at that stage due to the primitive laws in Australia around this topic.

Unfortunately, I found it very difficult to get anywhere near a doctor as I didn't have a place of residence, which was needed to make an appointment, and therefore no one would give me the time of day.

For those of you new to this concept, medicinal marijuana is prescribed by the doctor and that prescription is taken to a dispensary where the prescription is filled, just like a pharmacy would dispense pharmaceuticals. The dispensaries, I found, were closed to the public, so I couldn't get near the operators or plant experts to have a chat with them either and due to my time constraints, I had to head back to Australia without talking to anyone, still pretty determined and convinced that I was going to find out what I needed to know from home regardless and apply it myself. Dr. Google would have many answers, and I knew of a few people I could turn to for opinions so I felt confident that this might be the direction that I was looking for on the management side of the coin.

This is the one and only poem I ever wrote about the seizures and it was on the plane on the way back to Australia from the USA in 2013:

If I were to tell you that you could touch the sky

If I were to tell you that you just float on by

If I were to watch a crowd come to a stand

If I were to watch you melt into my hand

If I were to feel you fall apart

If I were to feel you detach from your heart

If I were to hear you let out a moan

If I were to hear you shake to the bone

If I were to hear you after your peak

If I were to hear you now so innocent and meek

If I were to feel your dribble on my arm

If I were to feel you resting so calm

If I were to watch your eyes rest upon me

If I were to watch you get up and flee

If I were to tell you that you were my hero

If I were to tell you that this all means zero

It's only a seizure, let's go get a beer

My darling, my love, you have nothing to fear!

I am here to expose you to information about the most medicinal plant known to man – Hemp. Medical miracles are a common occurrence when using oil derived from this specific medicinal plant.

Rick Simpson

CHAPTER 12

Permissions for Prescriptions

In 2014 it had been recommended that I have another EEG, which concluded that I still have uncontrolled electrical activity coming from the left side of my brain. The time had come for a radical approach to change the medication I was on that hadn't worked for three years, so I sat in the doctor's office and the plan was laid at my fingertips. The plan was to switch from Lamictal, which I had been on for three years, to Keppra, a stronger drug and at a higher dose, which was not exactly music to my ears. I asked the doctor to Google the side effects of Keppra for me and after reading about the potential of suicide, depression and anxiety, I took the prescription he wrote for me and left, with him thinking I was about to start this new drug regime. What I really knew in my head was I had one more stop to make before I committed to the rollercoaster ride experienced when changing medications – Next stop, Ganjatown!

Medicinal marijuana (MM) - a medicine provided straight from one of nature's healing plants, in order to minimise symptoms and assist people with their quality of life. Sounds fabulous and what every practitioner is looking for in regards to their patients' treatment... So, why is it such a globally controversial topic? Actually, this is the hardest chapter for me to write about because I have feelings on both sides of the coin about marijuana and its uses, effects and side effects, both for the treatment of epilepsy and as a herb in general.

I used marijuana recreationally for a very long time in my late teens and early twenties, both as a tool to have fun and also as an escape from the depressing reality that there was something "wrong" with me, which was slowly closing in. It became a reliable friend I could turn to, which would alleviate all my stressors and leave me feeling totally relaxed and able to pass out cold most nights. Most of my peer group at the time were smoking as well, so it was also used in many of my social situations. We never got into trouble while smoking 'ganja', as we were always too stoned to even be bothered getting into trouble. It was fun bonding and provided a somewhat medicinal purpose as it kept me relaxed and numbed my emotions. It was during my 20's that it stopped being fun and started to become more of a habit, then it became a routine and then it became something I couldn't be without, an addiction if you will.

After seven years of "self-medicating" and smoking large quantities daily, I got the feeling I had to kick the habit as the chilled vibe I used to smoke it for wasn't there anymore. Instead, waves of paranoia when I was stoned, had taken its place. Once I made the decision to stop, I got off it cold turkey and I made a vow to myself in the year 2000, when I was 28, never to touch marijuana again. My reasons then were that I didn't want to hide behind ANY drugs that numbed me or assisted in making me drowsy or depressed. So, I stopped the marijuana first, then took off to Northern NSW and got off the pharmaceuticals.

Many families are now using cannabis to successfully treat very severe childhood epilepsy (Dravet's syndrome), albeit, in Australia, illegally. Often when these families have run out of pharmaceutical options and their children are more or less having constant seizures, they have been more than willing to be arrested for possession and use of an illegal plant, if it meant they didn't have to see their child have upwards of 100 seizures a day. There are also a lot of encouraging stories in the media about cannabis being used to treat heaps of other conditions including pain, nausea, certain types of cancer, multiple sclerosis, Alzheimer's, anxiety, PTSD, arthritis, bowel inflammation and much more.

But, after decades of demonisation that started in the USA with the synthetic textile industry, cannabis is illegal in nearly every country and, as such, it has been difficult for doctors and scientists to research it properly to find out which strains are good for which illnesses and how much to administer, etc. It looks like the laws in Australia are going to change soon to allow access to marijuana as a medicine for certain illnesses, but it's a slow process for many who have loved ones with terminal illnesses, suffering debilitating pain or who aren't able to control their countless daily seizures. (3)

It took me 14 years from when I stopped smoking and made my "no pot" rule, to throw caution to the wind and try it as a medicine. I had known about MM for years but was always a bit hesitant to try it, as I didn't know much about it and thought that I would be off my face all day, every day and I didn't want to feel that way constantly just to avert a couple of seizures a month. In the early stages, I didn't even know it was possible to get preparations containing only CBD (cannabidiol) which is the non-psychoactive element of the cannabis plant. The preparations remove the Tetrahydrocannabinol (THC); the main psychoactive component of the cannabis plant leaving room for the medicine to work without feeling the psychoactive effects.

Cannabinoid receptors are present throughout the body, particularly in the brain and immune system but also in the peripheral nervous system, cardiovascular system, reproductive system, gastrointestinal and urinary tracts. Our bodies naturally produce compounds that interact with these receptors that are called endocannabinoids. (4)

Diary Entry:

9TH FEBRUARY 2014

I have been quite afraid of starting this journey with the MM because I have to totally rely on myself for my healing this time. For the last 20 years, I have been jumping from doc to neurologist, to naturopath, to spiritual healer, to herbs, yoga, reiki, you name it, and the list goes on. This time, because this method is highly unconventional, only slightly researched and not legal in Australia, I feel like I am on my own.

The other hesitation around starting the MM was that in order to keep up the medicine flow, I need to source the plant, make the same dose from the same strain and have it on call when I need it. This is the tricky bit because you can't just get the tincture from the chemist, or from the local supermarket or the like. It needs to come from the ground, organic ideally, no hydro stuff and that can cost a lot of money when you aren't growing it yourself and buying it off other people. I was given some seeds to plant but I ain't no gardener, so god only knows what will happen to them. They are in the soil now and hopefully going to sprout soon because it seems I will run out of tincture before these babies come alive.

Luckily, I work in an area and know some people with knowledge and perhaps access to what I need. There are many people 'rooting' for me and I feel very blessed! I have told all my friends, some of my family and people at work. I really am, as far as I am aware, the first person in my circle of people, to embark on this experience and throw myself in hammer and tongs to see what happens on the other side. Does this make me brave or mad??

I found out about this guy making tincture for his teenage son, who was living with ADHD so, I paid him a visit to find out more about it. My dad happened to be up visiting, so I schlepped him along with me to this guy's house for a bit of moral support. Let me tell you a little about the house. There was so much shit on the veranda, you could hardly see the door but we eventually found it through a vortex of boxes and a lovely man welcomed us into his house. This man had seven kids living with him and, despite the fact his home looked like a cyclone had gone through it, he seemed to be in complete control of his world. I had no choice but to leave my judgements amongst the piles of dirty washing and full kitty-litter boxes, as he was my only link into marijuana as medicine at this stage and perhaps even my miracle cure?!

I received the tincture made for me from the CBD-rich strain, which contained no THC, or if so, a negligible amount. In many cases it's not the tincture itself which is the legal concern as the amount of cannabis used is so low that it's hardly traceable. The illegality of the medicine simply falls with the cultivation, possession and supply of cannabis plants to produce the medicine. He very kindly didn't charge me and the only instruction that came with it was how to activate the drops, so the medicine works faster, and that was to put it in a cup, add hot water and then a herbal tea of my choice. He believed that the hot water opens up the liquid faster than having it cold, and so the benefits would be seen quicker. I was told that three to five drops twice a day was a good start but to experiment with it, especially if I felt nauseous, in which case I should reduce it by a few drops. If I felt it wasn't working effectively, then I should bump up the dose. He had never made it for anyone with epilepsy before, so his recommendations were only guesstimates. This didn't bother me, as most of my experimentation with different plants and medicines were guesstimates as well. Once I left his home, the rest was up to me, as he obviously didn't want to be responsible for my experimentation and the potential effects.

I got two vials off this guy and, when they were nearly finished, I decided to start sourcing the plant myself as it would be cheaper and easier to have access to than buying it from other people. The plan was I'd extract and make a huge amount, enough to maybe last six months so at least I knew it would be a consistent strain I could count on. Problem was, because it's illegal in Australia, I was out on a limb on my own. Additionally, there weren't many knowledgeable people to discuss this with at the time, so I became a "self-medicating" user under no-one's guidance but my own, once again this wasn't unusual territory for me so I had no trepidation around it. I asked around a bit, got some friends involved in the process, and we made the medicine under my misinformed information. I kept dosing myself up on it because the amount I was taking was still leaving room for electrical misfires and the monthly Grand Mal but I really wanted it to work, so I persevered and kept increasing the drops thinking I would finally reach a dose where the electricity in my head would have to stop.

> Medical cannabis presents a conundrum for medical professionals. Its illegality in large parts of the world means most medical users are self-medicating and this also makes it a difficult drug to study in clinical trials.
>
> As a consequence, a significant proportion of medical cannabis research is based on self-reported use and outcomes, rather than large, carefully-designed, randomised trials.
>
> Professor Ian Olver, head of the Cancer Council of Australia

On a side note, I had started a relationship with a guy called Marty about three months before I started on the MM. I actually thought he might be a keeper, as he seemed to care for me deeply. He was so supportive of me and I even felt comfortable having seizures in front of him as I knew I would be in good, loving hands. Before I had a seizure in front of him we had discussed whether I wanted him to film me having one. I had considered getting someone to film me for years, but it's hard to watch someone you love have a Grand Mal seizure so it was probably not the first thing on their list of things to do for me at the time.

Marty, however was chomping at the bit to film me. I remember before the first Grand Mal episode he witnessed, I was very electric and things kept flying out of my hands due to me trying to continue doing things whilst my brain was misfiring. He kept pulling his phone out ready and eager to film and I remember saying "It won't happen, put the fucking thing away", (all in good humour of course). Most of the Grand Mal seizures I had, I told people it wasn't going to happen and to relax, as this electrical stage will pass over - of which 50% of the time it did. This time though, it didn't pass over so Marty's patience paid off and he got to film it. The Grand Mal was over in three minutes, the sleeping phase after was over in another five to ten minutes, the re-emergence into the conscious world was over in another five to ten minutes after that so after about 25 minutes all up, he was there to cuddle me afterwards which I hadn't experienced for over seven years.

Together, after the seizure, I watched myself on film for the first time. It was very confronting and not as bad as I had perceived it to be, but still extremely surreal. I remember looking at the recording of me on my side in full seizure mode, all tensed up and convulsing and drooling, and all I could see was the cellulite on my thighs jiggling around and thinking "Jesus I really should go to the gym more."

Things were going well until about two months after I started the MM. My dose was gradually getting higher and I was still on a small dose of Lamictal as well, in the hope I could wean off it altogether. I started to become very distant from Marty, unattracted to him all of a sudden, and also unable to let him get close to me on an intimate level, even hugging was off limits. I was becoming disconnected from everyone and feeling quite insular, depressed and apathetic. This is when it occurred to me that something wasn't right with the experiment I was doing on myself. Marty had been noticing for a while a significant change in me and was alluding to the fact that I should stop taking the drops, but I was adamant to see the four month experimental phase through.

At the end of this experiment, and ultimately the relationship, I had hit a pretty dark place and decided to get off the MM. I basically threw my hands up in the air, yelled into a pillow for three days, and admitted defeat. I would have cried, but I was severely lacking in any emotional response due to my mental numbness at that point. I had no more healing ideas or optimism left in me to overcome the seizures at this point and the only option, as I saw it, was to store my belongings and go to Melbourne, stay with mum for a while and address things. I was ready to take the information I'd learnt over the years through both western medicine and herbal medicine and end my inner battle.

This recent journey with the medicinal marijuana was the icing on the cake in allowing me to see clearer about how external substances, be it medications or herbs can assist you with your chemical imbalances. However, if there is emotional turmoil or stress going on inside you, causing or adding to the imbalance, then your choice is either to deal with it holistically - i.e. emotionally, chemically, spiritually, mentally and physically, or live with it and address it with the pharmaceutical meds only. Either way, as I have learnt, there needs to be no suffering or self-judgement in the process

I am still undecided on my feelings about marijuana. Recreationally, I don't use it because I really get a kick out of interacting with people, and if I am stoned I lose the ability to talk and I don't want to deny people of that! Medically, I would try it again down the track if it was available in consistent medicinal doses from a strain that is scientifically grown for my particular case, as well as grown, prescribed and manufactured by professionals. I believe in the healing qualities of the plant, but it's the same as any other medicine out there; it all relies on trial and error. No one can make a blanket claim that it will help everyone who has epilepsy or other conditions, as everyone's chemical makeup and issues are different, so it is just another experiment one would need to try for themselves and work out if it's the right medicine to help. Hopefully soon this will be a legal option for Australians. I was self-medicating with a plant that is designed to sedate and as I wasn't making the medicine properly, it was working against me. If the plant was legalised and was allowed to be made by experts for particular conditions instead of being criminalised, this sort of self-medication experimentation would not be necessary.

It's no wonder a people's movement has grown up around the cultivation, processing and use of this extraordinary plant medicine. However cannabis containing THC is still illegal despite its massive usefulness in treating a variety of serious illnesses. Let's hope that politicians and medical professionals will soon see sense and overcome the entrenched irrational views that exist around cannabis, botanical medicines, and the failed 'war on drugs'! (5)

The pro medicinal marijuana fighters out there are fervent in their fight for the freedom of the plant, which is great and extremely necessary, as I doubt we would have come this far without the voice of the people. What needs to be pointed out is that it isn't going to be a success story for everyone. The trials previously and currently being done thus far are more for severe childhood epilepsy, and untreatable epilepsy, not the Grand Mal tonic-clonic episodes, absence seizures, temporal lobe and myoclonic epilepsy that many adults and teenagers endure. For many, these baby steps that our government is taking to legalise marijuana for any medical purpose is happening way too slowly, and when it does become legalised the real challenge will be how to keep it out of the patenting hands of the pharmaceutical industries that potentially may set a price on this medicine that is too high for the consumer to even afford.

Like any drug, cannabis has its side effects, although what's interesting with medical cannabis is that the effects most sought after by recreational users are generally the effects most avoided by medical users.

The product that is beginning to emerge globally is one that is bred and used for largely recreational purposes and so these are strains now which contain a much higher concentration of the psychoactive component, which is THC, and that isn't necessarily the most useful component.

Many people who consume this product medicinally actually don't like this effect, they choose strains, say for example in the US, that are much lower in THC concentration and higher in the cannabidiol concentrations.

In parts of the world where medical cannabis is legal, considerable effort has gone into developing strains of marijuana that are carefully tailored for medical use, to reduce the unwanted side effects and boost the more desirable ingredients.

Dr David Caldicott
from the Australian National University and Calvary Hospital in Canberra

While there are anti-epileptic drugs available that control most epileptic symptoms, understanding the underlying mechanism of epilepsy could revolutionize treatment and perhaps improve current drug therapies. Additionally, proper understanding of the mechanism could perfect a diagnosis down to the specific brain dysfunction.

Carly Cenedella

CHAPTER 13

The Drug War

The whole "Lainie Chait drug debate" has been a very contradictory affair indeed. There are, of course, many different definitions of what a drug is but the two classifications that get the most attention in this story are pharmaceutical drugs and recreational drugs. I want to clarify that I'm not writing this in order to bag pharmaceutical drugs or the medical profession. I'm also not writing this to encourage recreational drug use. They are both medicines and it is simply our personal perception of what a drug is and how and why it is consumed that determines, in all of us, what is and is not acceptable. The difference for me was, I could choose my recreational band-aid to suit the mood that I wanted to experience and I would embark on that chosen journey, whereas the prescribed medication and its outcome felt like a daily jail sentence that I couldn't escape and thus I only saw the negatives.

I have never had a moral issue consuming recreational drugs. I've basically been on one drug or another since I was 15. Cigarettes, marijuana, alcohol, anti-convulsants, MDMA and cocaine, never coffee thankfully. The cigarettes, weed and alcohol were what I was consuming before diagnosis. I was a teenager so I didn't know of any side effects, nor would I have really cared. This was way before the day that pictures of rotting teeth, arteries and feet were plastered on cigarette packets, so all we knew about smoking and its effects was a smokers cough and possibly death, but the latter was too far-fetched to contemplate so it didn't carry any merit.

Years later, the attraction to recreational drugs for me was that they made me feel awesome and allowed me to feel a separation from the everyday worries of my life. With this came the next day serotonin depletion, toxic liver and kidneys, hangover, or just basic exhaustion from being up late or all night, partying, with no sleep. I started to take note that there might be some damage being done, but still, I never made enquiries about what was in the ecstasy tablets that I consumed and what the side effects might be. I never questioned the cocaine dealer as to whether the cocaine was cut with toxins that were going to affect my brain in the long run, and the copious amounts of weed I smoked in my 20's encouraged a certain amount of apathy around questioning whether it was good or bad for me. I was probably so stoned at the time that, had I thought to ask questions, I would have forgotten them anyway.

I knew that taking ecstasy and other mood altering and expanding substances on the market was not holistically productive for me as a regular occurrence, but I could justify it at the time because it wasn't making the seizures worse and it was opening me up to lots of wonderful and fun experiences.

What I mean by the seizures not getting worse is that I would still have them due to my lifestyle choices and triggers i.e. lack of sleep, alcohol, and drugs, but they didn't occur if I was mindful that I needed to take time away from partying to sleep and eat properly as well. Through my years of self-analysis, observation and journaling to better understand my brain and its foibles, I was able to choreograph my life in a way so that I was able to party and partake in drugs and alcohol whilst at the same time trying to keep the seizures to a minimum. Looking back on it, it was way more destructive than helpful but it was what I went with at the time.

In all the years that I lived like this I can only recount one incident where I had a public display of break dancing, epilepsy style. I had been drinking and had taken some MDMA that night and my friends and I were having a great time but it was time to move the party from my house to a club in Melbourne that we frequented most weekends. I was feeling great, dancing, drinking and hanging with my buds. I suddenly started to feel really tired so I sat down on a couch with one of my oldest and dearest friends Tara, and then started to have a few head hiccups. There we were sitting on this couch, just hoping the misfires would work themselves out. I felt safe being with her but the music was getting louder, the MDMA had kicked in big time, and I suddenly started to feel really claustrophobic. The misfires were coming harder and faster and luckily Tara was onto it and didn't panic. Her instinct was to throw a jacket over my face so no one would be able to see, and she basically sat there with me whilst I had this massive seizure in the club. I don't remember a thing until I came out of it 20 minutes later and we all left to go back to our house. They partied on back at the house and I was quietly devastated, embarrassed, and exhausted. I had pushed it too far and my brain had no mercy on me. I had been told!

When I first started taking pharmies at the age of 19 I didn't question anything. I knew that I wasn't happy about it but I had to put my trust and faith in the system because I didn't know anything about epilepsy and just believed that the doctors knew what they were doing. Between 1993 and 2000 I was dosed up big time on numerous medical cocktails Epilim, Tegratol, Rivotril, experimentally trying to find the winning combination that would make my symptoms disappear.

My meds and neurologists were changed numerous times in those seven years in order to try and get the recipe right, but I eventually lost faith in the whole system. I got it into my head that these medicines were solving one issue and creating many others and I was the one who had to live this life, not the doctors.

Something was very wrong with this system. Intuitively, my feelers came out, I became very skeptical and I took a very active, passionate approach towards finding out what these medications were doing to me. The neurologists were trying to help and do their job well, but when you are trying to prevent symptoms of a condition, a lot of it does come down to guess work as you are working with the tangible issues that you can see and test for. I was looking for someone to indulge me to help with the intangible issues. Why was I more electric before my period? Why was I more electric when I was stressed? Why did my brain misfire more in the mornings?

When I was first diagnosed, there seemed to be a bit more ego in the system and the neurologists may have thought that they knew the workings of the brain quite well. My neurologist now, 20 years down the track is actually admitting that they don't know much at all and there is so much more to learn about the wonder that is the human brain.

For some reason I never put the hours of anti-drug militia into the recreational medicines that I did (and still do) with the pharmaceuticals that have been prescribed to manage my seizures. Why, I wonder? There could be a myriad of answers, but I think my main reason for my anti-meds mantra was that they only deal with the symptoms without really curing anything, a band aid if you will. Medicines are prescribed, but every script a doctor writes is not an immediate success story, for some, far from it. The medicines come with side effects and as we are all different, the only way a doctor, or anyone for that matter, is going to know if a medicine will work for you, is if you trial it for a period of time, usually two to four weeks is a good amount of time to know if you are reacting to it well or not. Three months in is when the side effects will start to really show up and these would then have to be addressed, potentially with more drugs and possibly more side effects.

When you have a condition of any sort, you become a guinea pig in the medical world, especially right at the beginning of the diagnoses as you are an apprentice in the system. For some, the initial treatment works instantly and they have found their winning combo. For many others, you slowly start to be aware that, as amazing as the medical industry is and as lucky as we are to have such an advanced system, until your individual medicinal management plan starts to work, you are at the mercy of time.

It would be very challenging to work in the health industry. People are looking for specialists to fix them immediately and are willing to live with the side effects of particular medications in order to achieve their idea of optimum health – no symptoms, no pain. I believe

1/3 of all epilepsy sufferers gain little or no relief from medications.

that we all possess the ability to manage ourselves on many different levels. This, however, requires a lot of inner work and commitment to our health; working psychologically with ourselves and seeing where the source of our "dis-ease" is coming from. This is a very confronting process, as well as time consuming, and it requires commitment and understanding of yourself, but that is a whole other book. Why I've brought that up here is because so many people are so unhappy about the medicines they are on. They know that the medicines aren't working and are creating other problems, but they feel backed into a corner and afraid of leaving the medical comfort zone and therefore place a lot of power solely in their doctor's hands. I never believed it was only the doctors who had the answers for me and have therefore continued to have faith in myself to search for more answers of how best to manage my seizures.

Doctors play a vital role in society. We'd be screwed without them. They study long and hard and are trained to diagnose, prescribe and assist in making decisions for people that will aid them to function normally in society. Sadly though, they aren't trained to look beyond the realm of medical healing, and the health system isn't yet set up holistically so that the doctor is looking at the patient as a whole and not, in my case, as just an electrically abnormal brain.

A quote that I recently read by Dr David Perlmutter spoke volumes to me "... I am saddened by the fact that the billion-dollar psychotropic pharmaceutical industry is predicated on the idea that people will take a pill to treat symptoms, while the underlying disorder is ignored. So there's never any real focus on actually curing or even improving the root cause of the illness, let alone getting people off the medication...."

My triggers and my abnormal electrical activity were intensified by stress, emotions, and hormonal changes. This of course didn't show up on an MRI or an ECG because they weren't looking for it. It wasn't in their framework and, honestly, they were so busy doing everything else to help me find a diagnosis that the extra training and energy they would have needed to devote to be able to look at the larger, holistic picture would have been very astronomical and dare I say, inflexible. So this part of my condition went untreated and was not even addressed until I got actively involved in my own treatment.

After studying myself very closely for the past 16 years, reading books on epilepsy, meditating, listening to radio broadcasts of doctors on the topic, self-medicating, keeping logs of my seizures and triggers, changing diets numerous times and basically trying to really understand how my brain works, I can now sit in a doctor's office, whether they are a specialist in the field or a regular GP, and feel really confident that I know just as much, if not more about my condition than they do, and that together we can treat this holistically.

Doctors, in fact all practitioners, are a great asset to us, they are in the business to help heal people and I am grateful for their dedication to the rest of us. We however, are an even greater asset to ourselves especially if we get to know the workings of the brain or wherever the condition stems from and can start asking for what will help rather than just accepting what the doctors are guessing will work. The best management plan I could have hoped for was for me to be in the driver's seat of the outcome.

These days I partake minimally in recreational drugs and all night partying. When I do go out, I'd much rather have a few drinks, some herbal concoctions from the Happy Herb Company for energy and be asleep by the early hours of the morning so I can function the next day. All my friends know about my seizure talent now so if I was to have a cheeky evening, it goes without saying that they might need to get the mop out the next day and sweep me into a corner and then make me poached eggs on toast whilst they keep reminding me that it was not so bad and divert my attention to the fun stuff from the evening before. Gotta love your mates!

I am now working with my neurologist, Dr Terry O'Brien, and listening to his wisdom in his field, but also knowing that my own innate wisdom and life experience is something to NEVER ignore. My recommendation to anyone would be to find the right specialist that understands you. It will make the ride more enjoyable and always keep them in the loop with what you are going through.

I am currently on what Terry refers to as a "small dose" of medication (Keppra), 250mg once a day, that has allowed me to be seizure and electricity free for two years (as of July 2016). On the grand scale, the side effects are minimal compared with other drugs I have taken. I feel like punching walls every now and then, feel very complacent, have no real highs or lows and not much sex drive, but then again, those experiences might just be part of being human. I am still coming to terms with the fact that I need to take medication to earn this seizure free life that I so desperately wanted. It has definitely given me back my psychological freedom and so I do have a lot of respect for the drug that I'm on. I have accepted that I need medication for now, and I am also working on myself neurologically and psychologically to change my mindset and put the work in to isolate, recognise, and avoid the triggers that create that chemical misfiring in the first place. Drugs can only cover these triggers, they don't get to the root of them and I want to get to the source so I can eliminate the triggers and have a seizure free life without the drugs, if at all possible.

If our brain is the engine that powers us in our daily life, then we should get to know how it works and how we can control it in order to get where we want to go.

Joe Dispenza

CHAPTER 14

Reprogramming the Motherboard

Diary Entry:

2ND FEBRUARY 2015

I recently became six months seizure free on January 19th 2015. Before this date, I was using the six month goal as a time in the future when I would get really excited and dance around naked, throw a goat on a spit and invite my close friends around to celebrate. I'd then get drunk, have a seizure and we could do it all again six months later. This of course didn't happen. What did happen was I got naked and posted my triumph up on Facebook. It got a lot of likes and so much support from friends and loved ones near and far but, to be honest, I wasn't really feeling that excited about it deep down, so I'm glad I didn't organize the killing of a goat in advance.

The reason I didn't get excited is that I am still coming to terms with the fact I need medication to achieve this stress free, seizure free existence. It sounds fucking crazy even writing that I wouldn't just want the magic pill to tame the beast but I invested so much positive thinking, time and money into healing myself naturally for the last 15 years that I sort of felt like a fraud when I posted that FB update, which reflected to me my inner unease with the truth of the situation.

Part of my acceptance of the condition for now is also about accepting the meds as part of the healing process and not to see them as separate to the story. After all, they have given me my mental freedom back and doors are starting to open. The kind of doors that, when you walk through them you catch si in a skinny mirror opposite you, and you can't help bu reflection and think, "I'm damn hot and I can handle whateve you've got for me, universe."

Once I stopped having seizures in 2014, I finally made the mature decision to once and for all find a management plan that not only treated my electric brain, but also included addressing those underlying anxiety and self-loathing issues I created for myself which directly related to the seizures. I couldn't seem to do this at the same time as having seizures; maybe due to them being the cause of the anxiety and self-loathing, I'm not sure, but I turned to the aid of mindfulness-based stress reduction, life coaching and the Avatar course to assist me with the inevitable challenge of reprogramming my brain.

For YEARS, each month, just before I had a Grand Mal seizure, I would work myself up into such an anxious state that would, more often than not, make the outcome so much worse for myself. What was simply going to be just some head hiccups, then morphed into a Grand Mal seizure, peppered with an anxiety disorder, and garnished with some pre-recorded internal failure dialogue, which made for a very un-tasty recipe indeed! Along the way, some people mentioned that I should try meditation to deal with some of the mind stuff I go through. I have numerous diary entries over the last 15 years of attempting meditation, but due to the fact it wasn't a quick fix and I had to do most of the work, I decided to feed my meditation practice to the dogs over and over again.

I tried the breathing, the sitting, the focusing on one spot, the audio in the background of whales farting, the mantras, the statues of Buddah on a shrine with incense burning and I just couldn't do it. As with everything that could have been beneficial for me, it was much easier to let it go than wrestle with it. That is of course until MBSR (Mindfulness Based Stress Reduction) crossed my path and I was ready to give meditation another go.

I had a friend come visit me who still reads raw, hard copied books - seems to be one of a minority these days. We wandered past a book shop and she naturally floated in all pumped up and excited. I, on the other hand, was out of my league because I hadn't picked up a book in years, so I had a wander around and gravitated towards the Mr Men books to see what Mr Silly had been up to for the last 20 years. As I was heading there a book basically jumped off the shelf and started harassing me to buy it, "The Healing Power of Meditation". What drew my attention to it, besides the fact it was on sale for five dollars, was that the book brought together Tibetan Buddhist teachers, scientific researchers, and health professionals to offer fascinating perspectives on the link between the mind and emotions. I bought it and ended up signing up for an eight week course two days later to see if I could take on the challenge to still my mind and sit peacefully, non-judgementally, and listen to the sounds of whales singing and farting.

MBSR is an intensive program used to complement the conventional medical management of a wide variety of illnesses. It allows people to mobilize their own inner resources of mind and body to become responsible for their personal health and healing. Something clicked during the course about the teachings of detachment to our thoughts, and it inspired me to keep up the practice even when the course finished. This mindfulness approach is the closest I have come to understanding what meditation is for and how it will benefit me. I don't have any personal evidence the mindfulness techniques I learnt will avert the seizures when and if they happen, but what I can say is this: it is teaching me how to change my way of thinking about everything, day by day.

It was straight after this that I committed to seeing a neuropsychologist once a week, who was essentially a psychologist specialising in brain related mental health conditions. I specifically sought her out as I thought I needed to outsource someone 'brain specific' to help me accept that I have this condition, and I wasn't convinced just any counsellor off the street would have a real grasp on the chemical workings of the brain in relation to nervous conditions.

She made for a good sounding board and I was making some progress with her, but it all seemed a bit too clinical for me, and I couldn't help feeling she was simply coming up with responses related to my script, without the drive to explore the issue further. This type of therapy works for some, but I felt like I needed someone to go deeper with me. This was only going to happen if someone was willing to get on their knees and jelly wrestle with me mentally in order to overcome my filthy, disproportionate outlook of myself. I was taking large steps towards accepting that epilepsy doesn't define me, but the seizures had defined my life for so long and had played such a big role in my lack of direction, lack of self-worth and warped belief systems that the confronting question I had to ponder was "Without epilepsy defining me, who am I?"

With this question in tow, I started to see a life coach because I was so inspired by my dear friend Christine's transformations whilst undertaking the steps to become a life coach, that I agreed to do a few sessions with her to see what it was all about. One of the first things to show up in the life coaching sessions was that I had programmed myself as a teenager to disassociate with my symptoms and hide them, and as time went on I cultivated this negative association that because I have seizures, I am a failure and no one will like me if they see me have a fit. Not only will they not like me, but they will leave me if they know the truth – that I'm not perfect! This was my belief system, my created platform that everything else has been built on ever since. No one had instilled this in me, except me!

As optimistic as I tried to remain over the years, I continued to be a failure in my own eyes, even though I could see so many personal successes in my determination to look at this condition laterally and heal myself outside of the medicinal system.

A brilliant exercise I heard about and committed to do, was to carry a pad and pen with me for two weeks, so I could write down every thought that entered my mind no matter how ridiculous – "I want some chocolate", "Reality television sucks", "Is that a new wrinkle on my forehead?", "Why do triceps have to sag as you get older?", "He has massive feet"... anything and everything that came to mind I wrote down because no one was going to see it except me. At the end of the fortnight I was astounded when I re-read my thoughts. I acknowledged 85% of the thoughts in my head on a daily basis were around seizure activity, and the embarrassment and anxiety I carried relating to those thoughts. It was life changing for me, really; to think, if I'm putting this amount of energy every day into these negative thoughts, what hope do I have of becoming free from them? Things changed there and then and I was on a mission to reprogram my thoughts and crack my belief system wide open.

This is where the Avatar journey I embarked on enters the picture. Avatar has only come about in the last couple of months for me and this internationally renowned self-development course gave me a bird's eye view of what my belief systems are and how I run my life based on these beliefs. It was a nine day intensive course in the USA designed to be an experiential journey. This means that they taught me how to get out of my head, where I've been surviving in and making all my decisions for decades, and into my body to start to feel again.

The journey with epilepsy has been such an intellectual one for me. I completely shut down my heart and emotions in order to deal with trying to hide myself from people, so much so that I completely forgot how to let anyone in.

Through Avatar, I saw just how shut off I was, how disconnected to myself I was and when I peeled back the layers of my belief systems, especially around epilepsy, I was confronted by having to look directly into the eye of the beast and take some personal responsibility for lots of things that I created around this condition. I will be writing more in depth articles about this journey on my website but Avatar was the greatest gift I have given to myself ever as I now have the tools to discreate old beliefs and only create things that are from my highest self.

There's a never ending orgy of healing modalities you can search through to find your own winning platform of health. An holistic approach to all illnesses seems to be the way the mindset is changing for many people. Holistic health is actually an approach to life. Rather than focusing on illness or specific parts of the body, this ancient approach to health considers the whole person and how he or she interacts with his or her environment. It emphasizes the connection of mind, body, and spirit. Within the framework of holistic health, people accept responsibility for their own level of well-being, and everyday choices are used to take charge of one's own health.

I'm not needing to "heal" the seizures anymore, just prevent them by existing within a space of self-love, allowing myself to be loved by others, and knowing I can always retreat to bring myself back to a healthy mind state by not attaching to the chatter in my head. Learning how to reprogram my brain and disconnect from my outdated belief systems, will ultimately lead to those old unconscious mantras about failure and abandonment being so far back in the neural network that they don't even show up on the grid. I recommend this to anyone, especially those who live with seizures, anxiety and depression, and carry shame and self-hatred with them.

Your body has the ability to
completely HEAL ITSELF of ANY disease...
All it needs is your assistance.

Dr. Richard Shulze

CHAPTER 15

Yours, in Light and Electricity

For years I managed my diagnosis of epilepsy really badly. In fact, people who know me would be amused by the fact I'm even using the word "manage" in relation to my condition. The only way I knew how to manage was to live my life as if I didn't have it and then deal with it when I did. I knew some of the triggers were emotional but didn't put a whole lot of effort into caring about them in my early 20's.

In my 30's I looked deeper into the triggers and did a lot of emotional searching and psychological unravelling, got off the meds and found herbs and alternative therapies which therefore meant management became more health related over time. Admittedly, I didn't wear a halo during my 30's and my health suffered somewhat for a couple of years due to drugs, alcohol and sacrificing sleep on odd occasions, but it was a decade full of trying my best to live by a healthy dogma 80% of the time. I documented my seizures, so I was well aware of the correlation between them and when I'd had a big night out, a fight with my boyfriend, or was approaching menstruation time. By the way, 85% of my seizures were just before I got my period which is a very common symptom for a lot of women and referred to as catamenial epilepsy.

Sixteen years ago, I couldn't wait to get out of the clutches of my life in Melbourne and disappear to a place where I could find people who were going to help me expand my knowledge regarding health and inner happiness and who would understand my plight towards a healthier approach to living with my seizures. The disappearing act was not necessarily to run away, but to create a space between what other people thought would be good for me and what I wanted to achieve for myself, which was a work in progress. Everyone wanted me to have peace, stability and acceptance of my situation, but the way that was going to happen for me was being out in the real world, doing my own research and not being boxed into a diagnoses with only one path to managing it, taking medicine!

As mentioned throughout the book, I have always been a victim of my fear of missing out personality, but I'm dealing with it much better in my 40's as I have adopted a much more appropriate acronym for my current stage in life – KYLT (Know Your Limits and Triggers). This theory still allows me to explore life and all it has to offer, without the fear of missing out on something amazing; knowing where I need to set my boundaries and when to reign in the 'party mode' in order to take time out for myself and rest. This is something I never even thought to contemplate at 17, as the mission statement was very different.

It's a bit cliché but we all have a message to impart and one of the only things that kept my head above water through this whole journey was knowing that, one day, I was going to put my story in writing and this would hopefully encourage all people afflicted with a condition to take the reins a bit more in their treatment, and for teenagers and young adults diagnosed with any condition where they feel helpless and isolated. It was the only anchor I could grasp onto that made the hundreds of seizures worthwhile.

For anyone reading this who is affected by seizures, especially teenagers, I highly recommend you start a journal. This journal should be used to document all things happening during your day and the emotions attached to it. If you get warnings, auras, misfires in your brain, or absences, start writing down all the things that happened just before or just after. Look at your diet and journal it for a while, so you can see if what you are eating affects your seizures.

Look at your sleeping patterns and stress levels and document them. Miscommunications, fights with siblings or friends, great nights out, indulgences with alcohol or other substances, sugar intake, menstruating, stress at work or school, a date that didn't call back, homework deadlines missed, whatever. Document it all and down the track you will start to see patterns that will help you understand yourself and your seizures much better and prove that you indeed have the power to manage and/or even prevent them simply by eliminating stress factors.

When you keep a journal of all these things, you start to feel like you have some control over a condition that would otherwise take control of you, if you let it. Every time you have a thought that sparks a trigger, document it and soon you will be able to read your way to your freedom. You'll be able to see firsthand how your actions can lower your seizure threshold. Some of us have a higher threshold than others when it comes to seizures. Things like lack of sleep, stress, bright lights or having a fight with a partner, friend or sibling can be all it takes to trigger a seizure. If it's all documented in front of you, it can't be random. It's real life evidence and the potential key to your acceptance. Medicine is just one way to assist with your seizures, but truly knowing yourself and when and why your seizures happen, even if it's linked in with genetics, will put the ball back in your court.

I used a spreadsheet, where I recorded everything occurring in the days leading up to my electrical brain farts, as well as any post-seizure observations. This became my bible and reading back through it after many months of documenting showed me exactly where my faith should be – in me! The column headings are up to you but be honest with yourself when writing stuff down; there's no point lying to yourself. This table was an idea from a friend of mine who has very high anxiety and had been filling his out for years, which helps him to manage his condition. It can be done for anything really, it just needs a bit of honest commitment and a desire to change your situation.

Headings on the spreadsheet included:

- Date
- Seizure or electricity
- Days since last seizure
- If electricity, when and how long did it last?
- Where in cycle?
- Was I alone?
- What meds/herbs am I taking?
- Quality of sleep leading up
- Alcohol
- Food
- Did I self-medicate prior?
- What did I take?
- Post seizure injuries?
- General comments

I have been very hard on myself for 20 years or more and I never gave myself self-love or nurturing about my situation. I am now two years seizure free and have been writing this book for 16 years waiting for that time when the story ended and I could lay it to rest. I desperately wanted to heal myself of these seizures, both unmedicated and organically, because I thought the story would have more merit with the desired outcome of being seizure free unmedicated, plus I wanted to look at myself in the mirror and see a hero, Electro Girl, that cured herself of epilepsy.

Luckily, now, I see a hero anyway and woke up to the fact I may still have epilepsy, but the story is well and truly over. The cure was in my self-acceptance and vulnerability all along. As resilient as this journey has made me, as much as I have tried to think that I could have done this on my own, I have been so lucky and blessed to have the unconditional support of my beautiful family in this very difficult journey. They have watched from the sidelines and just accepted I had to go off and live various lifestyles. Some massively destructive, others highly positive. They have had to suck up the worry and angst and hope and pray that I remained safe. As much as they would have liked to slap me around a bit and say "just fucking grow up and stop hurting yourself"... they didn't.

It's only been in the last six years that I have been the most honest and appreciative of them all. I talk more openly about it, they have seen and understood more of the triggers and how my brain can just misfire when I'm talking about something emotional. They understand, maybe don't agree, but understand, why I need to do things both pharmaceutically and alternatively, and we have all become closer because of this. This is a much better outcome for everyone as now, they know they can be honest with me about how it affected them without feeling that it might trigger off a seizure if they told me what they really thought. During the whole process, I was completely unaware of how censored their observations were but they didn't want to rock the boat and tip me over the edge. Did I unconsciously design it this way so I could have these experiences to myself with no one's input? Very possibly!

Recently I was interviewed for a radio show by a woman from the ABC (Australian Broadcasting Corporation) in Lismore about my story with epilepsy. It felt so good to finally be free of the embarrassment and shame around it and speak with even a sense of pride about my journey. I listened to myself talk and I felt like I was a professor on a subject that I'd been studying for years. I may not have a degree on paper but I have a PHD in Grand Mals to prove my experience and knowledge. I have been studying seizures, medications, side effects, alternatives, diets and the workings of the brain for 23 years and I believe that I am pretty well versed to have an opinion, now, that could stand up in a room full of brain experts. My answers to some of her questions made me see how challenging I've made this journey for myself. How isolating, painful, embarrassing, egotistical, and stubborn I've been in some ways, but it also pointed out how resilient I have been, how courageous, how liberated, how determined and how focused. I was on a mission way back in the year 2000 to take this condition in my own hands and deal with it accordingly, without being boxed into a corner by the medical profession and being labelled as ILL.

The negative outcome of 25 years of Grand Mal seizures, both treated and untreated, are: my memory is pretty tragic, my acceptance of it up to this year has been far from ideal. (I developed a secondary anxiety disorder around my condition). I have a scar on the bridge of my nose from a fall that is very evident, my two front teeth are veneered from smashing them and I'm still sceptical of the medical industry. But I am definitely going to leave this planet, when all is said and done, very impressed with myself and with a very good understanding of the way our brains work and just how incredible and lucky we are to have the blessing of CHOICE.

I have just recently witnessed my first public seizure from someone at work. The whole time that I have had them, I have only witnessed one in the hospital when I was 19. It was an interesting feeling as I witnessed this person at work completely taken over by the electrical misfires in her brain. I was suddenly confronted with my own thoughts of feeling that I don't know what to do and then almost immediately I felt a calmness within because I wasn't afraid of what was displaying in front of me, if anything life had thrown this reflection at me as a sign. I couldn't help thinking to myself, this is what it's all about! This is what the last 25 years have been about. Electro Girl must now rise up and use her magic to eliminate the fear for onlookers and educate and instil some calmness.

I feel like I have now graduated from the college of life with a PhD in 'how to live with and manage epilepsy effectively'. Join me on the journey to find your own inner super hero and bring this character to life! The most valuable thing I learnt in this whole story was to believe in myself and to harness the power within whilst keeping an open mind and being aware of all my options so that I could remain in the driver's seat and steer the ship! You are a step away from owning your condition and choosing the ultimate path of management for yourself.

With the universal awakening of our collective consciousness taking place now, there's more healing energy coming into our world to help souls who want to mend than ever before. Which means, there's never been a better time to choose to heal and reclaim your body, mind and soul than right now. There are many medical practitioners that are stepping up and wanting to heal the person as a whole not just as their symptoms. The change starts with you!

Yours, in love, light and electricity
ELECTRO GIRL

References:

1) http://www.epilepsiemuseum.de/alt/body_therapieen.html

2) https://www.epilepsy.org.au/resources/for-media/facts-statistics-about-epilepsy

3) http://www.abc.net.au/austory/content/2015/s4331491.htm

4) http://www.happyherbcompany.com/medical-cannabis-benefits-cbd-oil

5) http://www.happyherbcompany.com/medical-cannabis-benefits-cbd-oil

Acknowledgements

It is hard to put into words how grateful and blessed I feel to have so many wonderful people in my life who have assisted me through my journey.

Thanks to Marty Durkan and Nancy Lehet for the initial proof reading and pulling me up on how bad my grammar was so that I could get it to the editor without looking like English was my second language. Thanks also to Siobhan Ashton for her finishing touches.

Extra special eternal gratitude to my angels who floated around me for many years and kept watchful eyes over me: Leora, Eliza, Nicki, Chandra, Ray, Nadine, Christine, dad, Sarah, Nicole and mum.

Gratitude goes to my sensitive brain and my own tenacity for not allowing me to be complacent, and always pushing me to step up as an evolved human.

A big shout out to science. Yey! Especially the researchers and voices of those that are trying to get the answers to the way our brain function in order to be able to treat specifically what doesn't make it function well. A massive shout out to the scientists and doctors who are the voices of information around the healing of the brain through neuroplasticity.

Big ups to all the plant activists and medicinal marijuana fighters who are making great leaps to help shift the perspectives of Australia and move the draconian laws we are living under in relation to using medicinal marijuana as a medicine for those that are suffering.

Thanks to all the people I've connected with in the writing and publishing industry. You have made the daunting task of turning a manuscript into a published book much less scary with your wealth of knowledge and care to share your tips and secrets to success. Much gratitude goes to Steph, my initial editor, whose finished product maintained the dignity of my story whilst still making the necessary changes to make it a great read.

So much respect for the talented Sarah Seahorse who worked with me to design and make the best Electro Girl super hero outfit I have ever seen

A massive thanks to The Love Press who took the job of designing and printing the book cover & pages for this story. They nailed it better than I could have hoped for. I love it!!

A universal thanks and gratitude to Jenny Ashton who has assisted me out of the goodness of her heart in learning patience, making this dream more of a reality than I thought possible and for making me think out of the square.

Lastly I'd like to thank you, the reader, for taking an interest in my journey and having the faith in yourself to investigate your own situation holistically, in order to live a life not defined and restricted by only one type of treatment. Whether you have bouts of brain electricity yourself, know someone who does, or just wanted to know more about what epilepsy means, I would never have pushed myself to finish this book without knowing you were out there.

About the Author

Electro Girl is Lainie Chait's first book about her raw and personal journey of living day to day with the fears, isolation and sometimes burden of having epilepsy. She decided to bring it out of her journal entries and into print in order to inspire and empower people who need encouragement whilst dealing with the daily grind of living with epilepsy or other nervous conditions.

She was diagnosed with idiopathic epilepsy at the age of 19, had never heard of it before the diagnosis and was not really interested in knowing about it after she was diagnosed either. The way she saw it there were three roads to go down at the time. Avoidance, rebellion or acceptance. Over 25 years of living with epilepsy and experiencing more than 250 grand mal seizures, she confidently admits to have travelled down all three roads in order to try and understand and make sense of what was going on in her brain to make it spark like it did. Each road she travelled led her down a tunnel of light and darkness due to constantly trying to find answers and desperately wanting to "cure" herself through a plethora of different healing modalities both medical and alternative.

Lainie currently resides in Melbourne, Australia. She has been seizure free for two years at the time of writing this book and owes this to her courage, self acceptance, stubborness to not accept being a medical experiment and ability to holistically manage her life physically, emotionally, nutritionally and mentally.

R.E.M
Raw Encounters Media

CPSIA information can be obtained
at www.ICGtesting.com
Printed in the USA
LVHW012224180520
655844LV00006B/766